MCDOUGAL LITTELL
— The —
AMERICANS
Reconstruction to the 21st Century

CURRICULUM

In-Depth Resources: Unit 4

The 1920s and the Great Depression

McDougal Littell
A HOUGHTON MIFFLIN COMPANY
Evanston, Illinois • Boston • Dallas

Acknowledgments

CHAPTER 12

Excerpt from "The Big Money," from *U.S.A.* by John Dos Passos. Copyright 1930, 1932, 1933, 1934, 1935, 1936, 1937 and renewed 1964 by John Dos Passos. Reprinted by permission of Elizabeth Dos Passos.

"Justice Denied in Massachusetts" by Edna St. Vincent Millay, from *Collected Poems*, HarperCollins Publishers. Copyright © 1928, 1955 by Edna St. Vincent Millay and Norma Millay Ellis. All rights reserved. Reprinted by permission of Elizabeth Barnett, literary executor.

CHAPTER 13

Excerpt from "Interview with Charles A. Lindbergh," in *The New York Times*, May 23, 1927. Copyright 1927 by The New York Times Company. Reprinted by permission of The New York Times.

Excerpt from "When the Negro Was in Vogue," from *The Big Sea* by Langston Hughes. Copyright 1940 by Langston Hughes. Copyright renewed © 1968 by Arna Bontemps and George Houston Bass. Reprinted by permission of Hill and Wang, a division of Farrar, Straus & Giroux, Inc.

Excerpt from *Inherit the Wind* by Jerome Lawrence and Robert Edwin Lee. Copyright, as an unpublished work, 1951 by Jerome Lawrence and Robert Edwin Lee. Copyright © 1955 and renewed 1983 by Jerome Lawrence and Robert E. Lee. Reprinted by permission of Random House, Inc.

Caution: *Inherit the Wind* is the sole property of the authors and is fully protected by copyright. It may not be acted by professionals or amateurs without formal permission and the payment of a royalty. All rights, including professional, amateur, stock, radio and television broadcasting, motion picture, recitation, lecturing, public reading, and the rights of translation in foreign languages are reserved. All inquiries should be addressed to the authors' agent: Harold Freedman, Brandt and Brandt Dramatic Department, 101 Park Avenue, New York, NY 10017.

CHAPTER 14

Excerpt from *We Had Everything but Money*, edited by Deb Mulvey. Copyright © 1992 by Reiman Publications. Reprinted by permission of Reiman Publications.

Excerpt from "Attack on the Bonus Army" by Lee McCardell, originally appearing in *The Baltimore Sun*, July 29, 1932. Reprinted by permission of The Baltimore Sun.

Excerpt from *In the Beginning* by Chaim Potok. Copyright © 1975 by Chaim Potok and Adena Potok, Trustee. Reprinted by permission of Alfred A. Knopf, Inc.

CHAPTER 15

Excerpt from "Money Changers in the Temple" by Charles E. Coughlin in *Vital Speeches of the Day*, July 1, 1936. Reprinted by permission of City News Publishing Company, Inc.

Excerpt from "4 Killed, 84 Hurt As Strikers Fight Police in Chicago" in *The New York Times*, May 31, 1937. Copyright 1937 by The New York Times Company. Reprinted by permission of The New York Times.

Excerpt from *Let Us Now Praise Famous Men* by James Agee and Walker Evans. Copyright 1939, 1940 by James Agee. Copyright © 1941 by James Agee and Walker Evans. Copyright © renewed 1969 by Mia Fritsch Agee and Walker Evans. Reprinted by permission of Houghton Mifflin Company. All rights reserved.

Excerpt from "César Chávez" from *Hard Times* by Studs Terkel. Copyright ©1970 by Studs Terkel. Reprinted by permission of Donadio & Olson, Inc.

Printed in the United States of America.

ISBN-13: 978-0-618-17609-0   ISBN-10: 0-618-17609-8

9 10 11 12 – MDO – 08 07 06

CHAPTER ⓯ The Great Depression Begins, 1929–1933

CHAPTER ⓯ The New Deal, 1933–1940

Name _____ Date _____

CHAPTER 12
Section 1

GUIDED READING *Americans Struggle with*
Postwar Issues

A. As you read this section, take notes to answer questions about postwar conditions in America and the fear of communism.

After World War I, many Americans feared that Communists would take over the country.

1. How did the Justice Department under A. Mitchell Palmer respond to this fear?	2. Why did Palmer eventually lose his standing with the American public?
3. How did the Ku Klux Klan respond to this fear?	4. Why did the Klan eventually lose popularity and membership?

Public opinion turned against labor unions as many Americans came to believe that unions encouraged communism.

5. Why was the strike by Boston police unpopular with the public?	6. Why did Massachusetts governor Calvin Coolidge become so popular?
7. Why was the strike at U.S. Steel unpopular?	8. How did President Wilson respond to the steel strike?

The American labor union movement suffered setbacks as union membership dropped.

B. On the back of this paper, briefly describe how **Sacco and Vanzetti** became victims of the Red Scare. Then explain how **John L. Lewis** improved the lives of coal miners.

CHAPTER 12

Section 2

GUIDED READING *The Harding Presidency*

A. On the back of this page, note four measures taken by the Harding administration to maintain world peace.

B. Complete this description of how the Fordney-McCumber Tariff worked against Harding's efforts to maintain world peace. On each blank, write **B** for Britain, **F** for France, **G** for Germany, or **U** for the United States.

(1)___ adopted the Fordney-McCumber Tariff to protect businesses in (2)___ from foreign competition. This tariff made it difficult for (3)___ and (4)___ to sell goods in (5)___ and, therefore, difficult to repay their war debts to (6)___. To get money to pay those debts, they demanded reparations from (7)___, and troops from (8)___ invaded the Ruhr, an industrial region of (9)___. To avoid a new war, (10)___ adopted the Dawes Plan. Under this program, investors from (11)___ made loans to (12)___. It used the money to repay war debts to (13)___ and (14)___. Then they used the same money to repay war debts to banks in (15)___. In effect, (16)___ was repaid with its own money. This arrangement caused bad feelings on both sides of the Atlantic.

C. In the blank boxes below, write one or two words that describe how each nation, person, or group felt about the issues listed.

1. Americans → Kellogg-Briand Pact	
3. Americans → Immigrants	
5. Harding → Administration scandals	

2. Britain and France → Dawes Plan	
4. Ohio gang → Public service	
6. Americans → Harding	

D. On the back of this page, note how the actions of **Charles Evans Hughes** and **Albert B. Fall** affected the reputation of the Harding administration.

CHAPTER

12

Section 3

GUIDED READING *The Business of America*

A. In the first column, write notes to describe how the inventions and trends of the 1920s changed American life. In the second column, write the name of a related company or product that contributed to the boom of the 1920s.

Invention or Trend	Effects of the Invention or Trend	Company or Product
1. Automobiles		
2. Airplane industry		
3. Alternating electrical current		
4. Modern advertising		
5. Installment plan		

B. Why should Americans in the 1920s have shown greater concern for their future? Note three things that were, or might have been, seen as "clouds in the blue skies of prosperity."

1.	2.	3.

C. On the back of this paper, explain the meaning of **urban sprawl.**

BUILDING VOCABULARY *Politics of the Roaring Twenties*

CHAPTER 12

A. Matching Match the description in the second column with the term or name in the first column. Write the appropriate letter next to the word.

_____ 1. installment plan

_____ 2. Fordney-McCumber Tariff

_____ 3. isolationism

_____ 4. urban sprawl

_____ 5. John L. Lewis

_____ 6. nativism

a. leader of United Mine Workers

b. spread of cities

c. prejudice against foreign-born people

d. raised import taxes to highest level ever

e. a policy of retreating from foreign affairs

f. allowed people to buy goods over time

B. Evaluating Write *T* in the blank if the statement is true. If the statement is false, write *F* in the blank and then write the corrected statement on the line below.

_____ 1. Calvin Coolidge was a pro-business president.

_____

_____ 2. Anarchists were those who only opposed socialism.

_____

_____ 3. As secretary of state, Charles Evans Hughes urged the major powers of the West to build up their arms.

_____

_____ 4. Communism is an economic and political system based on a single-party government ruled by a dictatorship.

_____

_____ 5. The trial and conviction of Sacco and Vanzetti was an example of the hysteria caused by the Red Scare of the 1920s.

_____

C. Writing Write a paragraph describing the scandals of the administration of Warren G. Harding using the following terms.

Ohio gang   **Teapot Dome scandal**   **Albert B. Fall**

Name _____ Date _____

SKILLBUILDER PRACTICE *Clarifying; Summarizing*

Although most Americans wanted a return to "normalcy" during the 1920s, scientific advances were already changing the present and shaping the future. Read about some of these developments below, and then write a summary of the passage in the space provided. (See Skillbuilder Handbook, p. R4.)

Medical Science Advances in medical research during the 1920s significantly lengthened life expectancy rates for Americans. Dr. Harvey Cushing, noted brain surgeon and teacher, made significant advances in neurosurgery. Biochemist Harry Steenbock discovered how to produce vitamin D in milk, helping to reduce the number of cases of rickets, a vitamin-deficiency disease that causes defective bone growth, especially in children. Also, in 1927, Philip Drinker, a professor at Harvard University, invented the iron lung, a device for forcing air in and out of the lungs of patients who suffered respiratory failure caused by polio or other diseases.

Other medical advances during the 1920s included improvements in the treatment of diphtheria, whooping cough, measles, and influenza. In 1922 alone, the death rate in the United States from diphtheria was 14.6 for every 100,000 people, down from 43.3 deaths in 1900.

Physics The 1920s also saw many advances in the field of physics. Nuclear physicist Arthur H. Compton won the Nobel Prize for his study of X-rays. At the University of California, Ernest O. Lawrence began development of the world's first cyclotron, a device that accelerates charged particles so they can be used in the study of atomic structure. In a more commercial area, the 1920s saw the first long-range transmission of a television signal, between New York City and Washington.

These developments and others caused philosopher Alfred North Whitehead to proclaim that scientists were "ultimately the rulers of the world."

Write your summary of the passage here.

_____

_____

_____

_____

_____

_____

_____

_____

_____

_____

_____

_____

CHAPTER 12

Section 1

RETEACHING ACTIVITY *Americans Struggle with Postwar Issues*

Finding Main Ideas

The following questions deal with the issues Americans confronted after World War I.

1. What were the Palmer raids?

_____

_____

_____

2. What did the Ku Klux Klan advocate?

_____

_____

_____

3. How did the quota system limit immigration? Which groups did it hurt the most?

_____

_____

_____

4. What prompted the steel strike of 1919?

_____

_____

_____

5. For what reasons did union membership decline during the 1920s?

_____

_____

6. What unions were open to African Americans?

_____

_____

_____

Name _____ Date _____

Matching

A. Complete each sentence with the appropriate term or name.

business affairs   Fordney-McCumber Tariff
Charles R. Forbes   Andrew Mellon
Dawes Plan   upper house
Albert B. Fall   Kellogg-Briand Pact
social reform   Charles Evans Hughes

1. In 1928, fifteen nations signed the _____, which renounced war as a national policy.

2. Under the _____, American investors loaned Germany billions of dollars to pay its war reparations to Britain and France.

3. As president, Warren G. Harding favored a limited role for government in _____ and _____.

4. _____, a member of Harding's so-called Ohio Gang, was caught illegally selling government and hospital supplies to private companies.

5. As Harding's secretary of treasury, _____ set about cutting taxes and reducing the national debt.

Evaluating

B. Write *T* in the blank if the statement is true. If the statement is false, write *w* in the blank and then write the corrected statement on the line below.

_____ 1. Russia was not invited to the U.S.-sponsored Washington Naval Conference in 1921 because it did not have a navy.

_____

_____ 2. A significant weakness of the Kellogg-Briand Pact was that it had no means of enforcement.

_____

_____ 3. The Dawes Plan caused great resentment among the United States, Britain, and France.

_____

_____ 4. For his role in the Teapot Dome Scandal, Secretary of the Interior Albert B. Fall became only the second sitting cabinet member to be convicted of a felony.

_____

_____ 5. President Harding died while in office in August 1923, the victim of an assassination.

_____

CHAPTER 12
Section 3

RETEACHING ACTIVITY *The Business of America*

Multiple Choice

Choose the best answer for each item. Write the letter of your answer in the blank.

_____ 1. The president who said "the chief business of the American people is business" was
    a. Warren G. Harding.
    b. Calvin Coolidge.
    c. Herbert Hoover.
    d. William Howard Taft.

_____ 2. The mode of transportation that began as a mail carrying service for the U.S. Post Office was the
    a. automobile.
    b. airplane.
    c. train.
    d. bicycle.

_____ 3. During the 1920s, Americans' average annual income rose by about
    a. 10 percent.
    b. 15 percent.
    c. 25 percent.
    d. 35 percent.

_____ 4. The famous Route 66 stretched from Chicago to
    a. California.
    b. Wyoming.
    c. Utah.
    d. New York.

_____ 5. The man known for making a historic transatlantic flight was
    a. Henry Ford.
    b. Will Rogers.
    c. Charles A. Lindbergh.
    d. F. W. Woolworth.

_____ 6. One industry that did not prosper during the 1920s was the
    a. farming industry.
    b. advertising industry.
    c. airline industry.
    d. automobile industry.

CHAPTER

12

Section 3

GEOGRAPHY APPLICATION: REGION

The Automobile Industry: Sign of the Times

Directions: Read the paragraphs below and study the graph carefully.
Then answer the questions that follow.

The automobile industry has been the single most important industry in the United States since the 1920s. The value of its products exceeds that of any other industry, and a prolonged decline in car sales is usually a sign that the entire U.S. economy is headed for rough times.

So many other industries—such as those producing oil, steel, rubber, plate glass, machine tools, plastics, and aluminum—are dependent on automobile production that cars are vital to the nation's economic health. For example, a very high percentage of the steel, rubber, and plate glass produced in the United States winds up in cars. Businesses such as road construction and car-insurance firms, filling stations, and car-repair shops owe their existence entirely to the automobile. The lodging industry would be much less widespread today without motels. (The word *motel* was created around 1925 as a blend of *motor* and *hotel*.)

The 1920s were a period of dramatic economic growth. Prices for cars actually fell during the decade, as assembly-line techniques permitted faster production. Early in the decade, 90 percent of all the world's cars were made in the United States. By 1930, about 23 million cars were registered in the United States, nearly three times the number registered just a decade earlier. The production of automobiles in 1929 was not surpassed in any single year until 1949.

Municipal governments scrambled to provide roads for the growing numbers of cars. To pay for the aggressive road-building campaign, property-tax revenue was soon supplemented by heavy borrowing and by the use of state funds. In the 1930s, the idea of tolls as a source for highway revenue had caught on.

Though the number of automobile registrations reveals the general health of the U.S. economy, a graph of automobile production reveals the fine points—the smaller ups and downs within boom-and-bust cycles. For purposes of contrast, the following graph shows automobile production for the decade of the 1930s as well as for the 1920s.

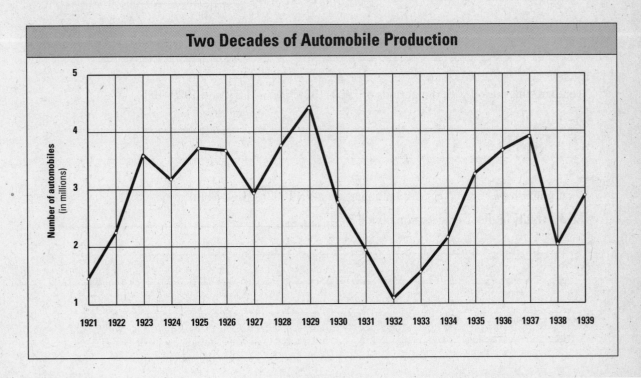

Two Decades of Automobile Production

Number of automobiles (in millions)

1921 1922 1923 1924 1925 1926 1927 1928 1929 1930 1931 1932 1933 1934 1935 1936 1937 1938 1939

Interpreting Text and Visuals

1. Characterize the general economic conditions in the United States during the
   decades of the 1920s and 1930s. _____

   _____

   _____

   _____

2. In what year was automobile production the highest? _____

   About how many cars were produced in that year? _____

   How many years did it take for annual sales to surpass that total? _____

3. What were the years of greatest economic decline between 1921 and 1939? _____

4. Describe the production of cars in 1932, in comparison to other years. _____

   _____

5. Between 1921 and 1929, there were two 13-month periods of economic downturn.
   During what years do you think they occurred? _____

6. What do you think happened to the economy in 1937–1938? _____

   _____

   _____

   Compare this period with the periods of 1923–1924, 1926–1927, and 1929–1932.

   _____

   _____

7. What might have spurred car production again after 1932? (Hint: Think about
   the durability of the average automobile.) _____

   _____

   _____

   _____

   _____

CHAPTER 12

Section 1

PRIMARY SOURCE *from* Bartolomeo Vanzetti's
Speech to the Jury

When Sacco and Vanzetti were arrested for murder and robbery in Braintree, Massachusetts, many observers believed the men were convicted because of their radical political views and Italian immigrant backgrounds. What does this excerpt from Vanzetti's last statement to the jury reveal about the trial?

Yes. What I say is that I am innocent, not only of the Braintree crime but also of the Bridgewater crime. That I am not only innocent of these two crimes, but in all my life I have never stole and I have never killed and I have never spilled blood. That is what I want to say. And it is not all. Not only am I innocent of these two crimes, not only in all my life I have never stole, never killed, never spilled blood, but I have struggled all my life, since I began to reason, to eliminate crime from the earth.

Everybody that knows these two arms knows very well that I did not need to go in between the street and kill a man to take the money. I can live with my two arms and live well. But besides that, I can live even without work with my arm for other people. I have had plenty of chance to live independently and to live what the world conceives to be a higher life than not to gain our bread with the sweat of our brow. . . .

Well, I want to reach a little point farther, and it is this—that not only have I not been trying to steal in Bridgewater, not only have I not been in Braintree to steal and kill and have never steal or kill or spilt blood in all my life, not only have I struggled hard against crimes, but I have refused myself the commodity of glory of life, the pride of life of a good position because in my consideration it is not right to exploit man. . . .

Now, I should say that I am not only innocent of all these things, not only have I never committed a real crime in my life—though some sins, but not crimes—not only have I struggled all my life to eliminate crimes that the official law and the official moral condemns, but also the crime that the official moral and the official law sanctions and sanctifies,—the exploitation and the oppression of the man by the man, and if there is a reason why I am here as a guilty man, if there is a reason why you in a few minutes can doom me, it is this reason and none else.

I beg your pardon. There is the more good man I ever cast my eyes upon since I lived, a man that will last and will grow always more near and more dear to the people, as far as into the heart of the people, so long as admiration for goodness and for sacrifice will last. I mean Eugene Debs. . . . He know, and not only he but every man of understanding in the world, not only in this country but also in the other countries, men that we have provided a certain amount of a record of the times, they all stick with us, the flower of mankind of Europe, the better writers, the greatest thinkers, of Europe, have pleaded in our favor. The people of foreign nations have pleaded in our favor.

Is it possible that only a few on the jury, only two or three men, who would condemn their mother for worldly honor and for earthly fortune; is it possible that they are right against what the world, the whole world has say it is wrong and that I know that it is wrong? If there is one that I should know it, if it is right or if it is wrong, it is I and this man. You see it is seven years that we are in jail. What we have suffered during those years no human tongue can say, and yet you see me before you, not trembling, you see me looking you in your eyes straight, not blushing, not changing color, not ashamed or in fear. . . .

We have proved that there could not have been another Judge on the face of the earth more prejudiced and more cruel than you have been against us. We have proved that. Still they refuse the new trial. We know, and you know in your heart, that you have been against us from the very beginning, before you see us. Before you see us you already know that we were radicals, that we were underdogs, that we were the enemy of the institution that you can believe in good faith in their goodness—I don't want to condemn that—and that it was easy on the time of the first trial to get a verdict of guiltiness.

We know that you have spoke yourself and have spoke your hostility against us, and your despisement against us with friends of yours on the train, at the University Club, of Boston, on the Golf Club of Worcester, Massachusetts. I am sure that if the people who know all what you say against us would have the civil courage to take the stand, maybe your Honor—I am sorry to say this because you are an old man, and I have an old father—but maybe you would be beside us in good justice at this time.

When you sentenced me at the Plymouth trial you say, to the best part of my memory, of my good faith, that crimes were in accordance with my principle,—something of that sort—and you take off one charge, if I remember it exactly, from the jury. The jury was so violent against me that they found me guilty of both charges, because there were only two. . . .

We were tried during a time that has now passed into history. I mean by that, a time when there was hysteria of resentment and hate against the people of our principles, against the foreigner, against slackers, and it seems to me—rather, I am positive, that both you and Mr. Katzmann has done all what it were in your power in order to work out, in order to agitate still more the passion of the juror, the prejudice of the juror, against us. . . .

Well, I have already say that I not only am not guilty of these crimes, but I never commit a crime in my life,—I have never steal and I have never kill and I have never spilt blood, and I have fought against the crime, and I have fought and I have sacrificed myself even to eliminate the crimes that the law and the church legitimate and sanctify.

This is what I say: I would not wish to a dog or to a snake, to the most low and misfortunate creature on the earth—I would not wish to any of them what I have had to suffer for things that I am not guilty of. But my conviction is that I have suffered for things that I am guilty of. I am suffering because I am a radical and indeed I am a radical; I have suffered because I was an Italian, and indeed I am an Italian; I have suffered more for my family and for my beloved than for myself; but I am so convinced to be right that if you could execute me two times, and if I could be reborn two other times, I would live again to do what I have done already. I have finished. Thank you.

from Osmond K. Fraenkel, *The Sacco-Vanzetti Case* (New York: Alfred Knopf, 1931). Reprinted in Henry Steele Commager, ed., *Documents of American History*, 7th ed., Vol. II (New York: Appleton-Century-Crofts, 1963), 218–219.

Discussion Questions

1. What crimes did Vanzetti maintain that he did not commit?
2. Did Vanzetti believe that Judge Thayer had been fair and impartial? Give evidence to support your response.
3. What accusation did Vanzetti make against the prosecuting attorney, Mr. Katzmann?
4. Vanzetti said he had suffered for his guilt. What "crimes" did he mention?
5. Some people liken the execution of Sacco and Vanzetti to the executions during the Salem witch trials in the 17th century. Do you agree with this comparison? Explain your reasons.

CHAPTER

12

Section 1

PRIMARY SOURCE *from* Report on the Steel Strike of 1919

A Commission of Inquiry appointed at the request of the Interchurch World Movement of North America prepared a report on the steel strike of 1919. The report included affidavits from more than 500 striking and nonstriking steel workers. As you read this portion of the report, consider why investigators recommended that the 12-hour day and 7-day week be eliminated.

It is an epigram of the industry that "steel is a man killer." Steel workers are chiefly attendants of gigantic machines. The steel business tends to become, in the owners' eyes, mainly the machines. Steel jobs are not easily characterized by chilly scientific terms. Blast furnaces over a hundred feet high, blast "stoves" a hundred feet high, coke ovens miles long, volcanic bessemer converters, furnaces with hundreds of tons of molten steel in their bellies, trains of hot blooms, miles of rolls end to end hurtling white hot rails along,—these masters are attended by sweating servants whose job is to get close enough to work but to keep clear enough to save limb and life. It is concededly not an ideal industry for men fatigued by long hours. . . .

First, what exactly is the schedule of the twelve-hour worker? Here is the transcript of the diary of an American worker, the observations of a keen man on how his fellows regard the job, the exact record of his own job and hours made in the spring of 1919, before the strike or this Inquiry, and selected here because no charge of exaggeration could be made concerning it. It begins:

"Calendar of one day from the life of a Carnegie steel workman at Homestead on the open hearth, common labor:

"5:30 to 12 (midnight)—Six and one-half hours of shoveling, throwing and carrying bricks and cinder out of bottom of old furnace. Very hot.

"12:30—Back to the shovel and cinder, within few feet of pneumatic shovel drilling slag, for three and one-half hours.

"4 o'clock—Sleeping is pretty general, including boss.

"5 o'clock—Everybody quits, sleeps, sings, swears, sighs for 6 o'clock.

"6 o'clock—Start home.

"6:45 o'clock—Bathed, breakfast.

"7:45 o'clock—Asleep.

"4 P.M.—Wake up, put on dirty clothes, go to boarding house, eat supper, get pack of lunch.

"5:30 P.M.—Report for work."

This is the record of the night shift; a record of inevitable waste, inefficiency and protest against "arbitrary" hours. Next week this laborer will work the day shift. What is his schedule per week? Quoting again from the diary:

"Hours on night shift begin at 5:30; work for twelve hours through the night except Saturday, when it is seventeen hours, until 12 Sunday noon, with one hour out for breakfast; the following Monday ten hours; total from 5:30 Monday to 5:30 Monday *87 hours, the normal week.*

"The Carnegie Steel worker works 87 hours out of the 168 hours in the week. Of the remaining 81 he sleeps seven hours per day; total of 49 hours. He eats in another fourteen; walks or travels in the street car four hours; dresses, shaves, tends furnace, undresses, etc., seven hours. His one reaction is 'What the Hell!'—the universal text accompanying the twelve-hour day."

from The Commission of Inquiry, The Interchurch World Movement, *Report on the Steel Strike of 1919* (New York: Harcourt, Brace and Howe, 1920), 58–60.

Activity Options

1. Imagine that you are either a steel worker or a steel mill official. Write a letter to the editor of a newspaper stating your opinion on the 12-hour day. Share your letter with the class.
2. Interview someone you know who works full time—a family member, a neighbor, a teacher—about his or her typical work day. Then compare this person's schedule with that of the steel worker in this excerpt.

CHAPTER 12

Section 3

PRIMARY SOURCE Advertisement

In the 1920s, advertising developed methods it continues to use today, over half a century later. Ads like Ned Jordan's 173-word classic, "Somewhere West of Laramie," used poetic language to glamorize automobiles. Who might this ad appeal to?

Somewhere West of Laramie

SOMEWHERE west of Laramie there's a broncho-busting, steer-roping girl who knows what I'm talking about.

She can tell what a sassy pony, that's a cross between greased lightning and the place where it hits, can do with eleven hundred pounds of steel and action when he's going high, wide and handsome.

The truth is—the Playboy was built for her.

Built for the lass whose face is brown with the sun when the day is done of revel and romp and race.

She loves the cross of the wild and the tame.

There's a savor of links about that car—of laughter and lilt and light—a hint of old loves—and saddle and quirt. It's a brawny thing—yet a graceful thing for the sweep o' the Avenue.

Step into the Playboy when the hour grows dull with things gone dead and stale.

Then start for the land of real living with the spirit of the lass who rides, lean and rangy, into the red horizon of a Wyoming twilight.

JORDAN

JORDAN MOTOR CAR COMPANY, Inc. Cleveland, Ohio

Corbis-Bettmann

Activity Options

1. With a small group of classmates, analyze this ad. What images and persuasive language does it use to sell the car? What attitudes does it portray? What information about the car does the ad include?

2. Find a car advertisement in a recent issue of a magazine. Then do a side-by-side comparison for the class in which you point out similarities and differences between the car ad you found and Ned Jordan's ad.

CHAPTER 12

Section 1

LITERATURE SELECTION *from* **The Big Money**
by John Dos Passos

In The Big Money *(1936), one of the novels in his trilogy, U.S.A., Dos Passos uses a series of shifting scenes to explore American life. In this excerpt, he focuses on the Sacco-Vanzetti case. The "newsreel" section intersperses news headlines with the lyrics to a song to give a feel for the times. The "camera eye" section records the narrator's stream-of-consciousness reactions. The paragraphs printed in italics are excerpts from Vanzetti's prison letters. Judging from this excerpt, how do you think Dos Passos felt about the Sacco-Vanzetti trial?*

NEWSREEL LXVI

HOLMES DENIES STAY

A better world's in birth

Tiny Wasps Imported From Korea In Battle To Death With Asiatic Beetle

BOY CARRIED MILE DOWN SEWER; SHOT OUT ALIVE

CHICAGO BARS MEETINGS

For justice thunders condemnation

Washington Keeps Eye On Radicals

Arise rejected of the earth

PARIS BRUSSELS MOSCOW GENEVA ADD THEIR VOICES

*It is the final conflict
Let each stand in his place*

Geologist Lost In Cave Six Days

The International Party

SACCO AND VANZETTI MUST DIE

Shall be the human race.

Much I thought of you when I was lying in the death house—the singing, the kind tender voices of the children from the playground where there was all the life and the joy of liberty—just one step from the wall that contains the buried agony of three buried souls. It would remind me so often of you and of your sister and I wish I could see you every moment, but I feel better that you will not come to the death house so that you could not see the horrible picture of three living in agony waiting to be electrocuted.

THE CAMERA EYE (50)

they have clubbed us off the streets they are stronger they are rich they hire and fire the politicians the newspapereditors the old judges the small men with reputations the collegepresidents the wardheelers (listen businessmen collegepresidents judges America will not forget her betrayers) they hire the men with guns the uniforms the policecars the patrolwagons

all right you have won you will kill the brave men our friends tonight

there is nothing left to do we are beaten we the beaten crowd together in these old dingy schoolrooms on Salem Street shuffle up and down the gritty creaking stairs sit hunched with bowed heads on benches and hear the old words of the haters of oppression made new in sweat and agony tonight

our work is over the scribbled phrases the nights typing releases the smell of the printshop the sharp reek of newprinted leaflets the rush for Western Union stringing words into wires the search for stinging words to make you feel who are your oppressors America

America our nation has been beaten by strangers who have turned our language inside out who have taken the clean words our fathers spoke and made them slimy and foul

their hired men sit on the judge's bench they sit back with their feet on the tables under the dome of the State House they are ignorant of our beliefs they have the dollars the guns the armed forces the powerplants

they have built the electricchair and hired the executioner to throw the switch

all right we are two nations

America our nation has been beaten by strangers who have bought the laws and fenced off the meadows and cut down the woods for pulp and turned our pleasant cities into slums and sweated the wealth out of our people and when they want to hire the executioner to throw the switch

but do they know that the old words of the immigrants are being renewed in blood and agony tonight do they know that the old American speech of the haters of oppression is new tonight in the mouth of an old woman from Pittsburgh of a husky boilermaker from Frisco who hopped freights clear from the Coast to come here in the mouth of a Back Bay socialworker in the mouth of an Italian printer of a hobo from Arkansas   the language of the beaten nation is not forgotten in our ears tonight

the men in the deathhouse made the old words new before they died

If it had not been for these things, I might have lived out my life talking at streetcorners to scorning men. I might have died unknown, unmarked, a fail-ure. This is our career and our triumph. Never in our full life can we hope to do such work for toler-ance, for justice, for man's understanding of man as how we do by an accident.

now their work is over   the immigrant haters of oppression lie quiet in black suits in the little undertaking parlor in the North End   the city is quiet   the men of the conquering nation are not to be seen on the streets

they have won why are they scared to be seen on the streets? on the streets you see only the downcast faces of the beaten   the streets belong to the beaten nation   all the way to the cemetery where the bodies of the immigrants are to be burned   we line the curbs in the drizzling rain we crowd the wet sidewalks elbow to elbow silent pale looking with scared eyes at the coffins

we stand defeated America

Research Options

1. Find out more about the life of either Nicola Sacco or Bartolomeo Vanzetti. Then write an obituary that might have appeared in a 1927 newspaper. Include relevant details about either Sacco or Vanzetti's life and death.
2. Find out about another prominent American writer or artist—besides novelist John Dos Passos and poet Edna St. Vincent Millay—who also supported Sacco and Vanzetti. Then explain to the class how this person voiced his or her opinions about the case.

CHAPTER
12

Section 1

LITERATURE SELECTION "Justice Denied in Massachusetts"
by Edna St. Vincent Millay

Edna St. Vincent Millay wrote this poem, which was published in **The Buck in the Snow and Other Poems** *(1928), after the executions of Sacco and Vanzetti. As you read the poem, think about its mood.*

Let us abandon then our gardens and go home
And sit in the sitting-room.
Shall the larkspur blossom or the corn grow under
   this cloud?
Sour to the fruitful seed
Is the cold earth under this cloud,
Fostering quack and weed, we have marched upon
   but cannot conquer;
We have bent the blades of our hoes against the
   stalks of them.

Let us go home, and sit in the sitting-room.
Not in our day
Shall the cloud go over and the sun rise as before,
Beneficent upon us
Out of the glittering bay,
And the warm winds be blown inward from the sea
Moving the blades of corn
With a peaceful sound.
Forlorn, forlorn,
Stands the blue hay-rack by the empty mow.
And the petals drop to the ground,

Leaving the tree unfruited.
The sun that warmed our stooping backs and
   withered the weed uprooted—
We shall not feel it again.
We shall die in darkness, and be buried in the rain.

What from the splendid dead
We have inherited—
Furrows sweet to the grain, and the weed
   subdued—
See now the slug and the mildew plunder.
Evil does overwhelm
The larkspur and the corn;
We have seen them go under.

Let us sit here, sit still,
Here in the sitting-room until we die;
At the step of Death on the walk, rise and go;
Leaving to our children's children this beautiful
   doorway,
And this elm,
And a blighted earth to till
With a broken hoe.

Discussion Questions

1. How does the poem's speaker feel after Sacco and Vanzetti are executed?
2. What images best convey the mood of this poem? Give examples.

3. Compare Millay's and Dos Passos's reactions to the Sacco and Vanzetti case.

CHAPTER 12

Section 2

AMERICAN LIVES Ernesto Galarza
Scholar, Educator, Activist

"When [Mexican-Americans] came to California, Anglo-Americans preached to us about our apathy and scolded us. . . . [But] what is mistaken for apathy is simply a system of self-defense. . . . 'La mula no nació arisca'—the mule isn't born stubborn, he's made stubborn."—Ernesto Galarza, "La mula no nació arisca" in Center Diary (September/October, 1966)

Ernesto Galarza, born in a small village in Mexico in 1905, came to the United States when he was six, one of hundreds of thousands of Mexicans who fled the turmoil of the Mexican Revolution. He became a scholar, an educator, and an activist.

Galarza was first involved in activism when he was in high school, while working picking crops. A teacher encouraged Galarza to pursue his education, and he went to college. Afterwards, he attended Stanford University for his master's degree and Columbia for his doctorate. While studying for his degree, he and his wife also launched their own school.

Galarza became a researcher for the Pan American Union. In ten years there, he studied a number of issues. Most prominent was the bracero program of the 1940s. During World War II, the United States suffered a shortage of farm workers. The government signed an agreement with Mexico to permit the entrance of temporary workers called *braceros*. At first the United States agreed to provisions required by Mexico that aimed to ensure that these workers were not discriminated against. In 1943, Congress allowed those limitations to be ignored if doing so was required for the war effort. With the limits lifted, the number of braceros jumped. The large growers used their economic power to take advantage of the workers. When other farm workers tried to organize and strike, the growers replaced those workers with braceros.

Galarza protested the bracero program. He believed that workers should be admitted to the United States as immigrants—so they could have the full rights of immigrants. Because he thought that the Pan American Union did not do enough to support the workers, he left that organization.

Meanwhile, Galarza was working for the National Farm Labor Union trying to organize farm workers. He led several strikes from the late 1940s through the mid-1950s. Each time, the union was defeated. He grew angry over the lack of support from organized labor, which was more interested in helping industrial workers. He also realized that the bracero program—still in force even though the war had ended—hampered moves to unionize farm workers.

In fighting the bracero program, Galarza was largely alone. One study describes his lonely effort: "He had neither large numbers of supporters, nor finances, nor friends in high places. His weapons were highly personal: the shield of research and analytical thought, the sword of the written and spoken word." One of those swords was his 1955 report, *Strangers in Our Fields*, a book based on a tour of 150 migrant-worker camps in California and Arizona. In 1964, he financed publication of another critical look at the growers, *Merchants of Labor*. That year, the bracero program was finally ended.

Over the next two decades, before his death in 1984, Galarza remained active in many ways. He taught at universities from Notre Dame to the University of California. He taught elementary school and—in San Diego—pioneered bilingual education. He wrote children's books in Spanish and in both Spanish and English. He helped organize community groups and advised foundations on Mexican-American issues. He had come far from the small village where he was born.

Questions

1. What does Galarza mean by using the Spanish saying about the mule?
2. What obstacles prevented the farm workers from organizing?
3. Why would a scholar and activist like Galarza become involved in elementary education?

CHAPTER 12

Section 3

AMERICAN LIVES **Henry Ford**
Engineer with a Vision

"[M]ake money and use it, give employment, build factories, and send out the car where the people [can] use it. . . . Business is a service, not a bonanza."
—Henry Ford, on his view of the goals of his business (1916)

Henry Ford (1863–1947) did not invent the automobile. He did not invent the assembly line. What he did was to use his engineering skill to develop a reliable car and to devise a method of manufacturing it that was cheap. In doing so, he achieved his vision—to put a steering wheel in the hands of ordinary people.

Ford was born on a farm outside Detroit and loved the peace of the countryside. He disliked farm work, though–machines interested him. At 16, he began to work in a machine shop. From that job and others he improved his knowledge of steam power and electrical systems. Meanwhile, he began to tinker with developing an automobile. In 1896, he completed his first, the "quadricycle," in a small shed. After knocking out part of the wall—the vehicle was too wide for the doorway—he drove his first car onto the street.

Ford sold the car for $200 and immediately began making another. Though his first two automaking companies failed, he earned a reputation as a skilled engineer. In 1902 Ford got the financial backing for a third company. Its first car was released in 1903. However, the investors wanted to sell cars to the wealthy—who bought most of the cars sold at the time. Ford wanted to make cars with mass appeal. He bought out these investors and in 1908 introduced his dream: the Model T. For almost 20 years, the Model T dominated the auto industry. By cutting costs, Ford was able to cut its price—from $1,000 in 1908 to only $345 in 1916. The durable, cheap "Tin Lizzie" became the everyday car of ordinary Americans. Much of the reduced cost of the Model T is attributed to Ford's unique assembly-line construction that eliminated unnecessary motion through simplified operations.

Ford also had another type of improvement up his sleeve. In 1914 he stunned American industry by announcing that he would pay workers $5 a day. As auto workers in Detroit were being paid from $1.80 to $2.50 a day, Ford's new wage was revolutionary. Ford's reasoning was simple: by paying workers more, he offset the boredom of the assembly line by giving them the resources to afford to buy his cars. Still facing some opposition from other investors, Ford bought out other stockholders and put control firmly in the hands of himself and his family. The cost was $105 million.

Ford suffered setbacks too. During World War I, he sponsored a "peace ship" that hoped to convince nations to stop the fighting. The idea failed miserably. He also became notorious for his extreme views, especially his hatred of Jewish people. Some workers resented the company's "Sociology Department." This group was set up to help workers—many of them immigrants and many uneducated—live thrifty lives. However, the staff often intruded in the workers' lives. Finally, during the 1920s, sales dwindled as consumers preferred flashier cars from other companies.

In 1927, Ford shut down his factories and helped design a new car—the Model A. It was an instant but short-lived success. The depression severely hit Ford's company. By the mid-1930s, Ford was only the third biggest automaker. In addition, the company had a poor labor-relations record. It suppressed union organizers until finally allowing a union in 1941.

Ford, meanwhile, devoted himself mainly to a new project. He founded a historical museum and village. This collection of homes and other buildings celebrated and preserved the values and lifestyle of nineteenth-century rural America—the life that Ford's car had changed entirely. After 1938 Ford mostly gave control of his company to others before officially retiring in 1945.

Questions

1. Hearing of the $5 day, a publisher said "He's crazy, isn't he?" Why did Ford's action get such a reaction?
2. Assess Ford's contribution to industry.
3. Do you think Ford was a good employer? Explain.

CHAPTER 13

Section 1

GUIDED READING *Changing Ways of Life*

As you read about how the 1920s reflected conflicts and tensions in American culture, take notes to answer the questions below.

In January 1920, prohibition went into effect.

1. a. Who tended to be supporters of prohibition at this time? b. Why did they support it?	2. a. Who tended to be opponents of prohibition at this time? b. Why did they oppose it?

3. Why was prohibition repealed?

In July 1925, Clarence Darrow and William Jennings Bryan faced each other in the Scopes trial.

4. a. Who were Darrow's main supporters? b. Why did they support him?	5. a. Who were Bryan's main supporters? b. Why did they support him?

6. What was the outcome of the case?

Name _____ Date _____

CHAPTER
13
Section 2

GUIDED READING *The Twenties Woman*

A. As you read about women's changing roles in the 1920s, fill out the chart by writing
notes in the appropriate spaces.

Social Life in the 1920s	
1. Note two ways women's fashions changed.	
2. Note two ways women's social behavior changed.	
3. Note two words that describe the attitude reflected by these changes.	

Work and Home Life in the 1920s	
4. Note one way women's work opportunities improved.	
5. Note two ways women's home and family life improved.	

6. Note three negative effects that accompanied women's changing roles in the 1920s.	

B. On the back of this paper, define **flapper** and **double standard**.

The Roaring Life of the 1920s **21**

CHAPTER
13
Section 3

GUIDED READING *Education and Popular Culture*

A. As you read this section, take notes summarizing how public education changed.

	Education Before the 1920s	**Education During the 1920s**
1. Enrollments		
2. Types of courses		
3. Immigrants		
4. Financing		

B. As you read about how America's popular culture developed in the 1920s, give at least two specific examples of each area of popular culture.

1. Magazines	2. Radio
3. Sports	4. Movies
5. Theater, music, and art	6. Literature

C. On the back of this paper, briefly explain who **Charles A. Lindbergh** was and how he became America's "most beloved hero" of the 1920s.

GUIDED READING *The Harlem Renaissance*

CHAPTER **13**
Section 4

A. Name the organization with which each leader was associated. Then note their beliefs and goals as well as the tactics they believed necessary to achieve them.

1. W. E. B. Du Bois and James Weldon Johnson	2. Marcus Garvey
Organization: _____	Organization: _____
Beliefs, goals, and tactics:	Beliefs, goals, and tactics:

B. Describe briefly what each of the following artists was known for.

African-American Writers
1. Claude McKay
2. Langston Hughes
3. Zora Neale Hurston

African-American Performers
4. Paul Robeson
5. Louis Armstrong
6. Duke Ellington
7. Bessie Smith

CHAPTER 13

BUILDING VOCABULARY *The Roaring Life of the 1920s*

A. Matching Match the description in the second column with the term or name in the first column. Write the appropriate letter next to the word.

_____ 1. Ernest Hemingway   a. made first nonstop flight across Atlantic

_____ 2. fundamentalism   b. banning of alcohol sale and consumption

_____ 3. Sinclair Lewis   c. flowering of African-American culture

_____ 4. prohibition   d. well-known American expatriate author

_____ 5. Marcus Garvey   e. underground saloons and nightclubs

_____ 6. Charles A. Lindbergh   f. winner of Nobel Prize in literature

_____ 7. Harlem Renaissance   g. belief in literal interpretation of the Bible

_____ 8. speakeasies   h. urged separate African American society

B. Completion Select the term or name that best completes the sentence.

George Gershwin   Bessie Smith   F. Scott Fitzgerald
Paul Robeson   Scopes Trial   Edna St. Vincent Millay
Louis Armstrong   Rough Riders   Georgia O'Keeffe

1. The _____ was a fight over evolution and the role of science and religion in U.S. public schools.

2. _____ helped create a uniquely American sound by mixing jazz with more traditional elements.

3. _____ was a prominent 1920s painter who sought to capture the grandeur of New York.

4. A tower figure of the Harlem Renaissance, _____ is considered perhaps the most important musician in the history of jazz.

5. An outstanding blues singer, _____ eventually became the highest paid black artist in the world.

C. Writing Bring the following two terms together in a paragraph about the dramatic changes women underwent in the 1920s.

flapper   **double standard**

CHAPTER

13

Section 3

SKILLBUILDER PRACTICE *Drawing Conclusions*

Just as Charles Lindbergh and other heroes of the 1920s provide insights into the mood of the decade, heroes of other eras can give us a sense of what those times were like and what people valued. Read the passage, then complete the chart with conclusions you draw about attitudes of the 1980s. Cite two supporting statements for each conclusion. (See Skillbuilder Handbook, p. R19.)

Traditional Heroes Through the centuries, societies have admired people who exemplified values such as courage, a willingness to sacrifice for others, and the strength to stand up for their beliefs at all costs. However, as conditions and values change, the kinds of heroes also change.

Heroes for the '80s In 1985, the magazine *U.S. News & World Report* commissioned a survey of young adults, 18 through 24 years old, to identify the people they most admired. The top ten heroes were (1) actor Clint Eastwood; (2) actor and comedian Eddie Murphy; (3) then-President Ronald Reagan; (4) actress and physical fitness advocate Jane Fonda; (5 and 6) a tie between actress Sally Field and movie director, writer, and producer Steven Spielberg; (7 and 8) a tie between Pope John Paul II and missionary Mother Teresa; (9 and 10) another tie between entertainers Michael Jackson and Tina Turner.

Most of the people on the list represent an optimistic, vigorous outlook. For example, President Reagan's dauntless positive outlook seemed unshak-

en, even after he had been shot by a would-be assassin in 1981. Likewise, the workout tapes and fitness books by Jane Fonda, then 47 years old, projected an image of youth and vitality.

Survey respondents pointed to the strong, courageous characters Eastwood and Field have played in their films. Eastwood's characters were tough, no-nonsense good guys; Field's were determined, struggling women who fought for what they believed.

Murphy and Spielberg drew praise for their creativity and remarkable box-office success, Murphy's ability to make people laugh, and Spielberg's direction of such films as *E.T.* and *Close Encounters of the Third Kind.* Likewise, the phenomenal energy and performance abilities of Michael Jackson and Tina Turner prompted their inclusion on the list.

Ironically, Pope John Paul II and Mother Teresa are the only people on the list whose personal lives actually fit the traditional sense of a hero. Their lives embody what some of the film characters represent—courage, sacrifice, and helping others. Also, these two are the only heroes who have not gained material wealth from their work.

Conclusion 1:

Support:

Support:

Conclusion 2:

Support:

Support:

CHAPTER
13
Section 1

RETEACHING ACTIVITY *Changing Ways of Life*

Finding Main Ideas

The following questions deal with the changing ways of life in America during the 1920s. Answer them in the space provided.

1. What were some pros and cons of life in the nation's cities?

_____

_____

2. For what reasons did some Americans promote Prohibition?

_____

_____

3. Why was the enforcement of Prohibition so difficult?

_____

_____

4. How did Prohibition help lead to the rise of organized crime?

_____

_____

5. Why did fundamentalists believe in a literal interpretation of the Bible?

_____

_____

6. What was the outcome of the Scopes trial?

_____

_____

CHAPTER 13

Section 2

RETEACHING ACTIVITY *The Twenties Woman*

Matching

A. Complete each sentence with the appropriate term or name.

nursing   social reform   managerial
factory   health-care   household labor
smoking   drinking   teaching
birth-control

1. After World War I, many female college graduates entered "women's professions," such as _____ and _____.

2. While some 10 million women were in the workforce by 1930, few had risen to _____ positions.

3. In 1916, Margaret Singer opened the first _____ clinic in the country.

4. A number of women in the 1920s displayed their new sense of freedom by _____ and _____ in public.

5. Women in the 1920s experienced greater freedom through the help of technological innovations that simplified _____.

Evaluating

B. Write *T* in the blank if the statement is true. If the statement is false, write *F* in the blank and then write the corrected statement on the line below.

_____ 1. Teenagers in the 1920s spent more time with their families than in decades before.

_____

_____ 2. As women experienced greater social and economic freedom, they also experienced greater equality in marriage.

_____

_____ 3. Fearing competition for jobs, many men argued that women should be just temporary workers.

_____

_____ 4. Traditionalists in churches and schools supported women's more freewheeling social behavior.

_____

_____ 5. The nation's birthrate, which had been declining for several decades, rose significantly during the 1920s.

_____

RETEACHING ACTIVITY *Education and Popular Culture*

Matching

A. Match the person in the first column with his or her accomplishments in the second column.

_____ 1. F. Scott Fitzgerald   a. wrote poems celebrating youth

_____ 2. Helen Willis   b. famous home-run slugger

_____ 3. Ernest Hemingway   c. made first solo flight across Atlantic

_____ 4. Edna St. Vincent Millay   d. dominated women's tennis

_____ 5. Babe Ruth   e. introduced simple, tough style of prose

_____ 6. Charles A. Lindbergh   f. wrote *The Great Gatsby*

Main Ideas

B. Answer the following questions in the space provided.

1. What prompted the sharp rise in high school enrollment during the 1920s?

_____

_____

2. How did radio have a strong impact on American society?

_____

_____

3. What major themes did the writers of the 1920s promote?

_____

_____

CHAPTER 13

Section 4

RETEACHING ACTIVITY *The Harlem Renaissance*

Matching

A. Complete each sentence with the appropriate term or name.

Great Migration	Marcus Garvey
James Weldon Johnson	anti-lynching

1. Between 1910 and 1920, million of blacks moved from the South to the North in search of jobs in what became known as the _____.

2. In 1914 _____ founded the Universal Negro Improvement Association, whose goal was to help blacks advance economically and socially.

3. During the early 1900s, the NAACP made _____ laws one of its main priorities.

Summarizing

B. Complete the chart below by listing various artists and their contributions regarding each aspect of the Harlem Renaissance.

Literature	Performance	Music

CHAPTER 13

Section 3

GEOGRAPHY APPLICATION: MOVEMENT

From Coast to Coast: By Train or by Plane?

Directions: Read the paragraphs below and study the map carefully. Then answer the questions that follow.

During the early 1920s, trains were the preferred means of long-distance travel in the United States. Airlines concentrated on fulfilling money-making postal contracts for carrying mail between cities. Carrying passengers was not profitable nor a priority. The 8 to 16 passengers per flight were assaulted by motor noise, cold drafts, vibration, and the dizziness of high altitudes. Most of them had to sign releases giving airlines the right to dump them anywhere along the route that mail bags could be picked up.

Then, in 1926, the Air Commerce Act was passed. Standards were established for pilot selection and flight equipment, and the day of thinking of flying as mostly for "daredevils" was nearing an end. By 1930 stewardesses (dressed in nurses' uniforms!) began serving on some flights. Comfort became a priority—as did speed.

In 1929, when a trip from New York to Los Angeles entirely by rail took about three days, a journey combining trains and planes brought that travel time down to less than two days, about 46 hours. At the time, commercial airliners were still not allowed to fly at night, so a plane would fly during the day, landing often to refuel. In the evening, its passengers would move by train overnight to a spot where a plane would be waiting to fly them to their next refueling stop along the way to their destination. Small towns with airports gained fleeting fame at the time.

The combination of air and rail travel lasted about 18 months, but it served to hook Americans on flying. In 1926 less than 6,000 people chose air travel; in 1930 the number was nearly 400,000.

By 1931, improved airplanes could fly greater nonstop distances and at night. In 1934 the trip from New York to Los Angeles was down to as little as 18 hours, with just three refueling stops.

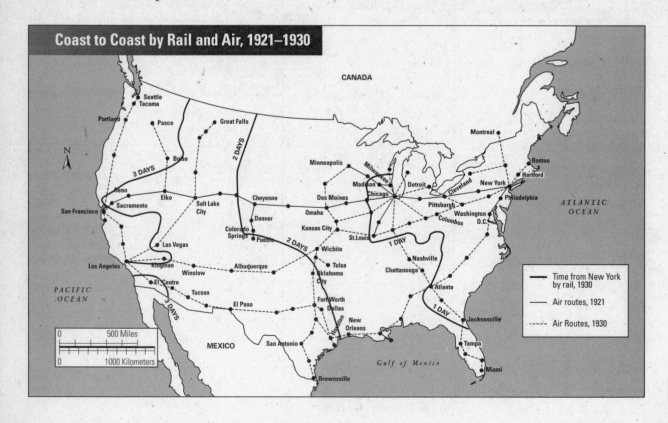

Coast to Coast by Rail and Air, 1921–1930

Legend:
— Time from New York by rail, 1930
— Air routes, 1921
--- Air Routes, 1930

Interpreting Text and Visuals

1. Imagine that it is 1925 and you live in Chicago. You have learned that a friend is about to fly to Salt Lake City. Make up a description of such a flight to warn your friend about what he or she might encounter.

   _____

   _____

   _____

   _____

2. In 1930 about how long did it take to travel by rail from New York to each of these places: Chicago, Denver, and Los Angeles? _____

   _____

3. In 1921, how many air routes served New York? served Chicago? _____

4. What were the final destinations of coast-to-coast flights in 1921? _____

   _____

5. What was the quickest time from New York to Los Angeles by air in 1929? in 1934? _____

6. What regions of the United States still lacked air routes in 1930? _____

   _____

   _____

7. It is 1921 and you want to fly from St. Louis to Cheyenne, Wyoming. Describe how you would get there. _____

   _____

   It is now 1929. How might you get to Cheyenne by air this time? _____

   _____

   _____

Name _____ Date _____

PRIMARY SOURCE Political Cartoon

*The hotly debated 18th Amendment, which prohibited the manufacture, sale,
and transportation of alcoholic beverages, went into effect in January 1920.
According to this political cartoon, what was the impact of prohibition?*

The Heritage of Prohibition, Herbert Johnson. Library of Congress

Discussion Questions

1. What effect of Prohibition does this cartoon
   illustrate?
2. According to the cartoon, what led to the growth
   of organized crime during Prohibition?

3. In the cartoonist's view, was Prohibition helpful
   or harmful? Explain your answer.

CHAPTER 13

Section 1

PRIMARY SOURCE *from* The Scopes Trial

The 1925 Scopes trial pitted defense attorney Clarence Darrow against special prosecutor William Jennings Bryan. Called as a defense witness, Bryan answered a blistering volley of questions fired at him by Darrow. As you read this transcript from the trial, think about which side—the fundamentalists or the evolutionists—prevailed.

DARROW: Mr. Bryan, could you tell me how old the earth is?

BRYAN: No, sir; I couldn't.

DARROW: Could you come anywhere near it?

BRYAN: I wouldn't attempt to. I could possibly come as near as the scientists do, but I had rather be more accurate before I give a guess. . . .

DARROW: Have you any idea how far back the last glacial age was?

BRYAN: No, sir.

DARROW: Do you know whether it was more than six thousand years ago?

BRYAN: I think it was more than six thousand years.

DARROW: Have you any idea how old the earth is?

BRYAN: No.

DARROW: The book you have introduced in evidence tells you, doesn't it? (*Darrow held up a copy of the Bible.*)

BRYAN: I don't think it does, Mr. Darrow.

DARROW: Let's see whether it does. Is this the one?

BRYAN: That is the one, I think.

DARROW: It says, B.C. 4004?

BRYAN: That is Bishop Usher's calculation.

DARROW: That is printed in the Bible you introduced?

BRYAN: Yes, sir. . . .

DARROW: Would you say the earth was only four thousand years old?

BRYAN: Oh, no; I think it is much older than that.

DARROW: How much?

BRYAN: I couldn't say.

DARROW: Do you say whether the Bible itself says it is older than that?

DARROW: I don't think the Bible says itself whether it is older or not.

(*a long pause*)

DARROW: Do you think the earth was made in six days?

BRYAN: Not six days of twenty-four hours.

DARROW: Doesn't it [the Bible] say so?

BRYAN: No, sir.

ATTORNEY GENERAL STEWART: I want to interpose another objection. What is the purpose of this examination?

BRYAN (*Pale and trembling, he rose, shaking his fist above his head.*): The purpose is to cast ridicule on everybody who believes in the Bible, and I am perfectly willing that the world shall know that these gentlemen have no other purpose than ridiculing every person who believes in the Bible!

DARROW: We have the purpose of preventing bigots and ignoramuses from controlling the education of the United States, and you know it, and that is all.

from L. Sprague de Camp, *The Great Monkey Trial* (New York: Doubleday, 1968), 401–404.

Activity Options

1. Re-create Darrow's cross-examination of Bryan. Have classmates take the following roles: Darrow, Bryan, Stewart, other members of the defense team, other members of the prosecution team, newspaper reporters who are covering the trial, and spectators who either support Bryan and the fundamentalists or Scopes, Darrow, and the evolutionists.

2. The Scopes trial highlighted the clash between evolutionists and fundamentalists. With a group of classmates, discuss some contemporary examples of the clash between science and religious beliefs.

PRIMARY SOURCE *from* An Interview with Charles A. Lindbergh

At the age of 25, Charles A. Lindbergh made his historic flight from Long Island to France in just under 34 hours. As you read part of an interview that Lindbergh gave after he arrived in Paris, think about how the public reacted to his accomplishment.

Well, here I am in the hands of American Ambassador Herrick. From what I have seen of it, I am sure I am going to like Paris.

It isn't part of my plans to fly my plane back to the United States, although that doesn't mean I have finished my flying career. If I thought that was going to be the result of my flight across the Atlantic, you may be sure I would never have undertaken it. Indeed, I hope that I will be able to do some flying over here in Europe—that is, if the souvenir hunters left enough of my plane last night.

Incidentally, that reception I got was the most dangerous part of the whole flight. If wind and storm had handled me as vigorously as that Reception Committee of Fifty Thousand, I would never have reached Paris and I wouldn't be eating a 3-o'clock-in-the-afternoon breakfast here in Uncle Sam's Embassy.

There's one thing I wish to get straight about this flight. They call me "Lucky," but luck isn't enough. As a matter of fact, I had what I regarded and still regard as the best existing plane to make the flight from New York to Paris. I had what I regard as the best engine, and I was equipped with what were in the circumstances the best possible instruments for making such efforts. I hope I made good use of what I had.

That I landed with considerable gasoline left means that I had recalled the fact that so many flights had failed because of lack of fuel, and that was one mistake I tried to avoid. . . .

The only real danger I had was at night. In the daytime I knew where I was going, but in the evening and at night it was largely a matter of guess-work. However, my instruments were so good that I never could get more than 200 miles off my course, and that was easy to correct, and I had enough extra gasoline to take care of a number of such deviations. All in all, the trip over the Atlantic, especially the latter half, was much better than I expected. . . .

I appreciated the reception which had been prepared for me, and had intended taxiing up to the front of the hangars, but no sooner had my plane touched the ground than a human sea swept toward it. I saw there was a danger of killing people with my propeller, and I quickly came to a stop.

That reception was the most dangerous part of the trip. Never in my life have I seen anything like that human sea. It isn't clear to me yet just what happened. Before I knew it I had been hoisted out of the cockpit, and one moment was on the shoulders of some men and the next moment on the ground.

It seemed to be even more dangerous for my plane than for me. I saw one man tear away the switch and another took something out of the cockpit. Then, when they started cutting pieces of cloth from the wings, I struggled to get back to the plane, but it was impossible. . . .

I look forward to the day when transatlantic flying will be a regular thing. It is a question largely of money. If people can be found willing to spend enough to make proper preparations, there is no reason why it can't be made very practical. Of course, there are many things to be studied, one of the most important points being whether the single-motor or multimotor ship is best. . . .

I didn't bring any extra clothes with me. I am wearing a borrowed suit now. It was a case of clothes or gasoline, and I took the gasoline. I have a check on a Paris bank and am going to cash it tomorrow morning, buy shirts, socks, and other things. I expect to have a good time in Paris.

But I do want to do a little flying over here.

from *New York Times,* May 23, 1927. Reprinted in Encyclopaedia Britannica, 1916–1928: *World War and Prosperity,* vol. 14 of *The Annals of America* (Chicago: Encyclopaedia Britannica, 1968), 557–561.

Research Options

1. If you could interview Lindbergh, what would you ask him about his flight? Jot down five questions and then find answers in a history book or encyclopedia.
2. Find out how the *Spirit of St. Louis* was similar to and different from airplanes today. Make a chart based on your research and share it with classmates.

CHAPTER 13

Section 4

PRIMARY SOURCE *from* "When the Negro Was in Vogue"
by Langston Hughes

Poet Langston Hughes was one of the leading voices of the Harlem Renaissance. What different aspects of life in Harlem does Hughes capture in this excerpt from his autobiography?

The 1920s were the years of Manhattan's black Renaissance. . . .

White people began to come to Harlem in droves. For several years they packed the expensive Cotton Club on Lenox Avenue. But I was never there, because the Cotton Club was a Jim Crow club for gangsters and monied whites. They were not cordial to Negro patronage, unless you were a celebrity like Bojangles. So Harlem Negroes did not like the Cotton Club and never appreciated its Jim Crow policy in the very heart of their dark community. Nor did ordinary Negroes like the growing influx of whites toward Harlem after sundown, flooding the little cabarets and bars where formerly only colored people laughed and sang, and where now the strangers were given the best ringside tables to sit and stare at the Negro customers—like amusing animals in a zoo.

The Negroes said: "We can't go downtown and sit and stare at you in your clubs. You won't even let us in your clubs." But they didn't say it out loud—for Negroes are practically never rude to white people. So thousands of whites came to Harlem night after night, thinking the Negroes loved to have them there, and firmly believing that all Harlemites left their houses at sundown to sing and dance in cabarets, because most of the whites saw nothing but the cabarets, not the houses. . . .

It was a period when, at almost every Harlem upper-crust dance or party, one would be introduced to various distinguished white celebrities there as guests. It was a period when almost any Harlem Negro of any social importance at all would be likely to say casually: "As I was remarking the other day to Heywood—," meaning Heywood Broun. Or: "As I said to George—," referring to George Gershwin. It was a period when local and visiting royalty were not at all uncommon in Harlem. And when the parties of A'Lelia Walker, the Negro heiress, were filled with guests whose names would turn any Nordic social climber green with envy. It was a period when Harold Jackman, a handsome young Harlem schoolteacher of modest means, calmly announced one day that he was sailing for the Riviera for a fortnight, to attend Princess Murat's yachting party. It was a period when Charleston preachers opened up shouting churches as sideshows for white tourists. It was a period when at least one charming colored chorus girl, amber enough to pass for a Latin American, was living in a penthouse, with all her bills paid by a gentleman whose name was banker's magic on Wall Street. It was a period when every season there was at least one hit play on Broadway acted by a Negro cast. And when books by Negro authors were being published with much greater frequency and much more publicity than ever before or since in history. It was a period when white writers wrote about Negroes more successfully (commercially speaking) than Negroes did about themselves. It was the period (God help us!) when Ethel Barrymore appeared in blackface in *Scarlet Sister Mary!* It was the period when the Negro was in vogue.

from Langston Hughes, *The Big Sea: An Autobiography* (New York: Hill & Wang, 1940).

Discussion Questions

1. How would you describe Harlem of the 1920s based on your reading of this excerpt?
2. Why do you think white America suddenly became fascinated by Harlem?
3. What is ironic about the situations described in this excerpt?

CHAPTER 13

Section 1

LITERATURE SELECTION *from* *Inherit the Wind*
by Jerome Lawrence and Robert E. Lee

In this excerpt from Act II of the play based on the Scopes trial, "Brady" repre-
sents the prosecutor William Jennings Bryan, "Drummond" is defense attorney
Clarence Darrow, "Cates" is John Scopes, and "Davenport" is Attorney General
Stewart. In your opinion, which man—Brady or Drummond—makes the
stronger case?

BRADY (*with dignity*): Your Honor, I am willing to sit here and endure Mr. Drummond's sneering and his disrespect. For he is pleading the case of the prosecution by his contempt for all that is holy.

DRUMMOND: I object, I object, I object.

BRADY: On what grounds? Is it possible that something is holy to the celebrated agnostic?

DRUMMOND: Yes! (*His voice drops, intensely*) The individual human mind. In a child's power to master the multiplication table there is more sanctity than in all your shouted "Amens!", "Holy, Holies!" and "Hosannahs!" An idea is a greater monument than a cathedral. And the advance of man's knowledge is more of a miracle than any sticks turned to snakes, or the parting of waters! But are we now to halt the march of progress because Mr. Brady frightens us with a fable? (*turning to the jury, reasonably*) Gentlemen, progress has never been a bargain. You've got to pay for it. Sometimes I think there's a man behind a counter who says, "All right, you can have a telephone; but you'll have to give up privacy, the charm of distance. Madam, you may vote; but at a price; you lose the right to retreat behind a powder-puff or a petticoat. Mister, you may conquer the air; but the birds will lose their wonder, and the clouds will smell of gasoline!" (*thoughtfully, seeming to look beyond the courtroom*) Darwin moved us forward to a hilltop, where we could look back and see the way from which we came. But for this view, this insight, this knowledge, we must abandon our faith in the pleasant poetry of Genesis.

BRADY: We must *not* abandon faith! Faith is the important thing!

DRUMMOND: Then why did God plague us with the power to think? Mr. Brady, why do you deny the *one* faculty which lifts man above all other creatures on the earth: the power of his brain to reason. What other merit have we? The elephant is larger, the horse is stronger and swifter, the butterfly more beautiful, the mosquito more prolific, even the simple sponge is more durable! (*wheeling on* Brady) Or does a sponge think?

BRADY: I don't know. I'm a man, not a sponge. (*There are a few snickers at this; the crowd seems to be slipping away from* Brady *and aligning itself more and more with* Drummond.)

DRUMMOND: Do you think a sponge thinks?

BRADY: If the Lord wishes a sponge to think, it thinks.

DRUMMOND: Does a man have the same privileges that a sponge does?

BRADY: Of course.

DRUMMOND: (*roaring, for the first time: stretching his arm toward* Cates): This man wishes to be accorded the same privilege as a sponge! He wishes to think! (*There is some applause. The sound of it strikes* Brady *exactly as if he had been slapped in the face.*)

BRADY: But your client is wrong! He is deluded! He has lost his way!

DRUMMOND: It's sad that we aren't all gifted with your positive knowledge of Right and Wrong, Mr. Brady. (Drummond *strides to one of the uncalled witnesses seated behind him, and takes from him a rock, about the size of a tennis ball.* Drummond *weighs the rock in his hand as he saunters back toward* Brady) How old do you think this rock is?

BRADY (*intoning*): I am more interested in the Rock of Ages, than I am in the Age of Rocks. (*A couple of die-hard "Amens."* Drummond *ignores this glib gag.*)

DRUMMOND: Dr. Page of Oberlin College tells me that this rock is at least ten million years old.

BRADY (*sarcastically*): Well, well, Colonel Drummond! You managed to sneak in some of that scientific testimony after all. (Drummond *opens up the rock, which splits into two halves. He shows it to* Brady.)

DRUMMOND: Look, Mr. Brady. These are the fossil remains of a pre-historic marine creature, which was found in this very county—and which lived here millions of years ago, when these very mountain ranges were submerged in water.

BRADY: I know. The Bible gives a fine account of the flood. But your professor is a little mixed up on his dates. That rock is not more than six thousand years old.

DRUMMOND: How do you know?

BRADY: A fine Biblical scholar, Bishop Usher, has determined for us the exact date and hour of the Creation. It occurred in the year 4,004, B.C.

DRUMMOND: That's Bishop Usher's opinion.

BRADY: It is not an opinion. It is literal fact, which the good Bishop arrived at through careful computation of the ages of the prophets as set down in the Old Testament. In fact, he determined that the Lord began the Creation on the 23rd of October in the Year 4,004 B.C. at—uh, at 9 A.M.!

DRUMMOND: That Eastern Standard Time? (*laughter*) Or Rocky Mountain Time? (*more laughter*) It wasn't daylight-saving time, was it? Because the Lord didn't make the sun until the fourth day!

BRADY (*fidgeting*): That is correct.

DRUMMOND (*sharply*): The first day. Was it a twenty-four-hour day?

BRADY: The Bible says it was a day.

DRUMMOND: There wasn't any sun. How do you know how long it was?

BRADY (*determined*): The Bible says it was a day.

DRUMMOND: A normal day, a literal day, a twenty-four-hour day? (*Pause. Brady is unsure.*)

BRADY: I do not know.

DRUMMOND: What do you think?

BRADY (*floundering*): I do not think about things that . . . I do not think about!

DRUMMOND: Do you ever think about things that you do think about? (*There is some laughter. But it is dampened by the knowledge and awareness throughout the courtroom, that the trap is about to be sprung.*) Isn't it possible that first day was twenty-five hours long? There was no way to measure it, no way to tell! Could it have been twenty-five hours? (*Pause. The entire courtroom seems to lean forward.*)

BRADY (*hesitates—then*): It is . . . possible . . . (*Drummond's got him. And he knows it! This is the turning point. From here on, the tempo mounts. Drummond is now fully in the driver's seat. He pounds his questions faster and faster.*)

DRUMMOND: Oh. You interpret that the first day recorded in the Book of Genesis could be of indeterminate length.

BRADY (*wriggling*): I mean to state that the day referred to is not necessarily a twenty-four-hour day.

DRUMMOND: It could have been thirty hours! Or a month! Or a year! Or a hundred years! (*He brandishes the rock underneath Brady's nose*) Or ten million years! (*Davenport is able to restrain himself no longer. He realizes that Drummond has Brady in his pocket. Redfaced, he leaps up to protest.*)

DAVENPORT: I protest! This is not only irrelevant, immaterial—it is illegal! (*There is excited reaction in the courtroom. The Judge pounds for order, but the emotional tension will not subside.*) I demand to know the purpose of Mr. Drummond's examination! What is he trying to do? (*Both Brady and Drummond crane forward, hurling their answers not at the court, but at each other.*)

BRADY: I'll tell you what he's trying to do! He wants to destroy everybody's belief in the Bible, and in God!

DRUMMOND: You know that's not true. I'm trying to stop you bigots and ignoramuses from controlling the education of the United States! And you know it! (*Arms out, Davenport pleads to the court, but is unheard. The Judge hammers for order.*)

JUDGE (*shouting*): I shall ask the bailiff to clear the court, unless there is order here.

BRADY: How dare you attack the Bible?

DRUMMOND: The Bible is a book. A good book. But it's not the only book.

BRADY: It is the revealed word of the Almighty. God spake to the men who wrote the Bible.

DRUMMOND: And how do you know that God didn't "spake" to Charles Darwin?

BRADY: I know, because God tells me to oppose the evil teachings of that man.

DRUMMOND: Oh. God speaks to you.

BRADY: Yes.

DRUMMOND: He tells you exactly what's right and what's wrong?

BRADY (*doggedly*): Yes.

DRUMMOND: And you act accordingly?

BRADY: Yes.

DRUMMOND: So you, Matthew Harrison Brady, through oratory, legislation, or whatever, pass along God's orders to the rest of the world! (*Laughter begins.*) Gentlemen, meet the "Prophet from Nebraska!" (*Brady's oratory is unassailable, but his vanity—exposed by Drummond's prodding—is only funny. The laughter is painful to Brady. He starts to answer Drummond, then turns toward the spectators and tries, almost physically, to suppress the amused reaction. This only makes it worse.*)

BRADY (*almost inarticulate*): I—Please—!

DRUMMOND: (*with increasing tempo, closing in*) Is that the way of things? God tells Brady what is good! To be against Brady is to be against God! (*more laughter*)

BRADY (*confused*): No, no! Each man is a free agent—

DRUMMOND: Then what is Bertram Cates doing in the Hillsboro jail? (*some applause*) Suppose Mr. Cates had enough influence and lung power to railroad through the State Legislature a law that only *Darwin* should be taught in the schools!

BRADY: Ridiculous, ridiculous! There is only one great Truth in the world—

DRUMMOND: The Gospel according to Brady! God speaks to Brady, and Brady tells the world! Brady, Brady, Brady, Almighty! (*Drummond bows grandly. The crowd laughs.*)

BRADY: The Lord is my strength—

DRUMMOND: What if a lesser human being—a Cates, or a Darwin—has the audacity to think that God might whisper to *him*? That an un-Brady thought might still be holy? Must men go to prison because they are at odds with the self-appointed prophet? (*Brady is now trembling so that it is impossible for him to speak. He rises, towering above his tormentor—rather like a clumsy, lumbering bear that is baited by an*

agile dog.) Extend the Testaments! Let us have a Book of Brady! We shall hex the Pentateuch, and slip you in neatly between Numbers and Deuteronomy! (*At this, there is another burst of laughter. Brady is almost in a frenzy.*)

BRADY (*reaching for a sympathetic ear, trying to find the loyal audience which has slipped away from him*) My friends—Your Honor—My Followers—Ladies and Gentlemen—

DRUMMOND: The witness is excused.

BRADY (*unheeding*): All of you know what I stand for! What I believe! I believe, I believe in the truth of the Book of Genesis! (*beginning to chant*) Exodus, Leviticus, Numbers, Deuteronomy, Joshua, Judges, Ruth, First Samuel, Second Samuel, First Kings, Second Kings—

DRUMMOND: Your Honor, this completes the testimony. The witness is excused!

BRADY (*pounding the air with his fists*): Isaiah, Jeremiah, Lamentations, Ezekiel, Daniel, Hosea, Joel, Amos, Obadiah— (*There is confusion in the court. The Judge raps.*)

JUDGE: You are excused, Colonel Brady—

BRADY: Jonah, Micah, Nahum, Habakkuk, Zephaniah— (*Brady beats his clenched fists in the air with every name. There is a rising counterpoint of reaction from the spectators. Gavel.*)

JUDGE (*over the confusion*): Court is adjourned until ten o'clock tomorrow morning! (*Gavel. The spectators begin to mill about. A number of them, reporters and curiosity seekers, cluster around Drummond. Davenport follows the Judge out.*)

Activity Options

1. Perform this excerpt from *Inherit the Wind* with a group of your classmates. Be sure to pay attention to stage directions for tips on gestures, tone of voice, and so forth.

2. Compare the dialogue in this excerpt with what Darrow and Bryan said during the court trial (on page 33). Then discuss the similarities and differences with a small group of classmates.

CHAPTER 13

Section 3

AMERICAN LIVES Georgia O'Keeffe
Abstract Painter

"I have used [my art] to say what is to me the wideness and wonder of the world as I live in it."—Georgia O'Keeffe, quoted in World Artists *(1984)*

In 1915, Georgia O'Keeffe became dissatisfied with everything she had painted until then. So she destroyed almost all of it. She then started over, developing a style that made her one of the most important of all American artists.

O'Keeffe showed artistic talent when young and studied in both Chicago and New York. She even won an award for a still-life painting. However, the work dissatisfied her. It seemed merely to imitate a style that was accepted. "I began to realize that a lot of people had done this same kind of thing," she later recalled. "I didn't think I could do it any better." She stopped painting and took work as a commercial artist.

Illness forced her to abandon that work five years later. After taking an art class, she became interested in the simplified style of Oriental art. The interest quickened her desire to begin art again. First, though, she destroyed almost all the art she had created until then. She began to draw some charcoals in which she reduced real objects to their most abstract form. She sent them to a friend in New York, with the instruction to reveal them to nobody else. The friend, disobeying, showed the work to Alfred Stieglitz, an art dealer and photographer. Stieglitz was so impressed he began to exhibit the drawings in his gallery. When O'Keeffe found out, she protested. However, Stieglitz calmed her down, and they began a professional and personal relationship that lasted the rest of his life. They were married in 1924, but most important, Stieglitz encouraged O'Keeffe to paint whatever she liked.

She did so—for more than 60 years. O'Keeffe became famous for her spare, clean work. She drew, painted in watercolors, and painted in oil. She created small studies only 7-by-9 inches and huge canvasses that were 8-by-24 feet. She painted flowers, doors, barns, and the sky—whatever interested her. Many of her paintings are so realistic that they have been called photographic. Yet underlying them all is an abstract feeling for the form of the object. Often she painted the same object repeatedly. In each canvas, the object became less and less recognizable. The last work in the series shows the forms and colors of the object, which can no longer be recognized as an object.

O'Keeffe painted what was around her. When she first settled with Stieglitz in New York, she painted the moon and sun over city buildings. They had a summer home on a lake, and she painted the flowers she saw there. Later she visited New Mexico and became enchanted by its landscape. Many of the works painted there show the bleached bones of cattle or horses. Critics said this work showed a preoccupation with death. O'Keeffe denied it. "There was no rain, so the flowers didn't come," she said. "Bones were easy to find, so I began collecting bones." Among her most well-known works are a series looking at the sky through the holes in an animal skull.

She returned to New Mexico each summer after that. When Stieglitz died in 1946, O'Keeffe moved there permanently. Later, she began to travel extensively to Europe and the Orient. Flying gave her new subjects. She "noticed a surprising number of deserts and wonderful rivers. . . . You see such marvelous things, such incredible colors." She painted a new series that portrayed winding rivers framed in a landscape seen from the air.

O'Keeffe's approach was unique in American art. She refused to be categorized with one school of art or another. "I'm not a joiner," she said. She painted until her death at age 99.

Questions

1. Why did O'Keeffe not like her early work?
2. Would you say that O'Keeffe was more interested in natural or human objects? Explain your answer.
3. How is O'Keeffe's art both realistic and abstract?

AMERICAN LIVES Louis Armstrong

Jazz Master, Entertainment Superstar

CHAPTER 13

Section 4

"[Louis] Armstrong's story on records between 1923 and 1932 is one of almost continuous seeping growth—and after that is frequently one of entrenched excellence."—Martin Williams, **The Smithsonian Collection of Classic Jazz (1973)**

Louis Armstrong—known everywhere as Satchmo—was born in the poorest section of New Orleans and had a difficult early life. When he died, he was loved by millions as a popular entertainer. In between, he revolutionized jazz.

Armstrong (c. 1900–1971) grew up in Storyville, a part of New Orleans set aside for dance halls and other entertainment. In his early teens, he ran afoul of the law and was placed in a home for juveniles. The experience changed his life. There he began to learn to play the cornet and decided to become a musician. After leaving the home, he played in countless local bands. Soon his talent was noticed, and in his late teens he played with Joe "King" Oliver, the most admired cornet player in the city.

Oliver left for Chicago—recommending Armstrong to replace him in the band he left. A few years later, he invited Armstrong to join his Creole Jazz Band in the north. The band was famous in the world of jazz, and musicians flocked to hear Oliver's and Armstrong's duets on the cornet. Armstrong became known for the imagination and technical skill of his solo playing.

Amstrong traveled to New York to join the famous dance band of Fletcher Henderson. He perfected his ability to sight-read music and learned to appreciate ensemble playing. At the same time, he took the town by storm with dazzling solos. He returned to Chicago in 1925, switched to trumpet, and made jazz history.

Over the next few years, Armstrong made a series of records with a group of musicians called the "Hot Five" and the "Hot Seven." One music historian says that the cuts "transformed jazz," adding that "few performers [who came later]. . . escaped their influence." Jazz trumpeter Miles Davis put it differently: "You can't play a note on the horn that Louis hasn't already played." In these recordings, Armstrong manipulated complex rhythms. He showed range of feeling in his music, bringing greater emotion to jazz than had previously been the case. He also added his distinctive singing style to the group's work. He started scat singing—using the voice as an instrument by singing nonsense syllables. Most of all, he combined tight combo playing with spectacular solos. Through him, jazz became dominated by adventurous, masterful soloists.

In the early 1930s, he acquired his famous nickname "Satchmo." His importance as a jazz innovator peaked around 1937, and thereafter he became known more as an entertainer. He began to play more commercial music, and he did it with a winning style. His band became one of the popular big bands of the swing era. He became the first African American to appear regularly in movies and to have his own radio show. He toured the country—and the world—constantly. After World War II, the big-band sound lost popularity. So Armstrong formed a small jazz combo called "Louis Armstrong and His All Stars." He continued to delight audiences with his warm, joyful sound. As time passed, his lips became injured, so he played trumpet less and sang more. Even then, he could still thrill an audience with his playing. As one critic said, he "frequently created more pure jazz from straightforward statements of mediocre tunes than lesser players could produce from much better material."

Armstrong continued to be an entertainer through his sixties. In 1964, his version of "Hello, Dolly" even knocked the Beatles off the top of the pop-music charts for a while. While he closed his career as a popular musician, Satchmo's lasting achievement was the impact he had on jazz.

Questions

1. How did his experience with the Fletcher Henderson band help Armstrong musically?
2. What made Armstrong's jazz style special and influential?
3. Why was Armstrong's wide popularity unusual?

Name _____ Date _____

GUIDED READING *The Nation's Sick Economy*

Section 1

A. As you read this section, take notes to describe the serious problems in each area
of the economy that helped cause the Great Depression.

1. Industry	2. Agriculture

3. Consumer spending	4. Distribution of wealth	5. Stock market

B. On the back of this paper, explain or define each of the following:

Alfred E. Smith   Dow Jones Industrial Average

Black Tuesday   Hawley-Smoot Tariff Act

CHAPTER
14
Section 2

GUIDED READING *Hardship and Suffering During the Depression*

A. As you read about how people coped with hard times, use the chart below to summarize the Great Depression's effects on various aspects of American life.

1. Employment
2. Housing
3. Farming
4. Race relations
5. Family life
6. Physical health
7. Emotional health

B. On the back of this paper, define each of the following terms.

Dust Bowl   **shantytown**   **soup kitchen**   **bread line**   **direct relief**

Name _____ Date _____

CHAPTER 14
Section 3

GUIDED READING *Hoover Struggles with the Depression*

A. As you read about President Hoover's response to the Great Depression, write notes in the appropriate boxes to answer the questions.

Philosophy
1. What was Hoover's philosophy of government?

Responses and Economic Results
2. What was Hoover's initial reaction to the stock market crash of 1929?
3. a. What was the nation's economic situation in 1930? b. How did voters in 1930 respond to this situation?
4. a. What did Hoover do about the economic situation? b. How did the economy respond to his efforts?
5. a. How did Hoover deal with the economic problem posed by the Bonus Army? b. How did his efforts affect his own political situation?

B. On the back of this paper, explain the the main purpose of the **Reconstruction Finance Corporation** (RFC) and whether it succeeded in achieving that goal.

CHAPTER 14

BUILDING VOCABULARY *The Great Depression Begins*

A. Completion Select the term or name that best completes the sentence.

Calvin Coolidge	Dust Bowl	Federal Home Loan Bank Act
Buying on margin	Herbert Hoover	price-supports
Great Depression	Alfred E. Smith	Reconstruction Finance Corporation

1. In an attempt to help ease farmers' financial woes, the government began a policy of
_____, or buying surplus crops and selling them abroad.

2. The period from 1929 to 1940, in which the nation suffered from a continuous and deep economic crisis, was known as the _____.

3. Accompanying the economic depression of the 1930s were years of drought that earned the Great Plains the name _____.

4. The cautious steps taken by President _____ in addressing the Great Depression roused anger among many Americans.

5. President Hoover's most ambitious economic measure, the _____, authorized up to $2 billion for banks and other businesses.

B. Evaluating Write *T* in the blank if the statement is true. If the statement is false, write *F* in the blank and then write the corrected statement on the line below.

_____ 1. The day in October 1929 that the stock market crashed became known as Black Tuesday.

_____

_____ 2. Hoping to increase the flow of goods into the country, Congress in 1930 passed the Hawley-Smoot Tariff Act, which established the lowest tariffs in the nation's history.

_____

_____ 3. Direct relief was cash payments or food provided by the government to the poor.

_____

_____ 4. Many investors in the late 1920s began buying on margin, or purchasing stocks and bonds on the chance of a quick profit, while ignoring the risks.

_____

_____ 5. The group of World War I veterans who marched on Washington, D.C. to demand immediate payment of their war bonuses was known as the Rough Riders.

_____

C. Writing Write a paragraph about daily life during the Great Depression using the following terms.

shantytowns   **soup kitchens**   **bread lines**

CHAPTER
14
Section 2

SKILLBUILDER PRACTICE *Interpreting Graphs*

Depression statistics often have the most impact when shown graphically. Read the title of the graphs below to identify the main idea. Read the vertical and horizontal axes of the graphs. Look at the legends and note what each symbol and unit represents. What trends do you see over certain years? When you compare the two graphs, what conclusions can you draw? Write a paragraph to summarize what you learned from the graphs. (See Skillbuilder Handbook, p. R28.)

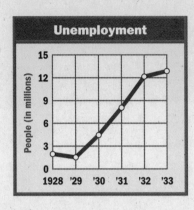

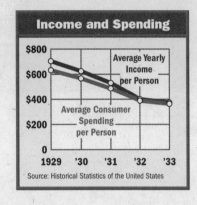

Write a Summary

Write a paragraph to summarize what you learned from the graph.

_____

_____

_____

_____

_____

_____

_____

CHAPTER

14

Section 1

RETEACHING ACTIVITY *The Nation's Sick Economy*

Analyzing

Complete the chart below by detailing how each entry adversely affected the nation's economy.

decline in the number of new homes built	
more Americans living on credit	
uneven distribution of wealth	
stock market crash of 1929	
widespread bank closings	
worldwide depression	
Hawley-Smoot Tariff	

CHAPTER
14
Section 2

RETEACHING ACTIVITY *Hardship and Suffering During*
the Great Depression

Finding Main Ideas

The following questions deal with the daily suffering during the Great Depression.
Answer them in the space provided.

1. What advantage did people in rural areas have over city-dwellers during the depression?

_____

_____

2. Why were conditions for African Americans and Latinos especially difficult during the
Depression?

_____

_____

3. What factors helped to cause the Dust Bowl?

_____

_____

4. How did the Depression affect the country's children?

_____

_____

5. Why did working women meet with such resentment during the Depression?

_____

_____

6. What social and psychological impact did the Depression have on Americans?

_____

_____

RETEACHING ACTIVITY *Hoover Struggles with the Depression*

Section 3

Completion

Choose the best answer for each item. Write the letter of your answer in the blank.

_____ 1. Early on, many economists thought the best way to battle the Depression was to
  a. suspend the income tax.
  b. offer cash handouts.
  c. let the economy fix itself.
  d. experiment with socialism.

_____ 2. One Hoover-initiated project that provided many jobs and aided California's growing agricultural economy was construction of the
  a. Boulder Dam.
  b. Brooklyn Bridge.
  c. Erie Canal.
  d. transcontinental railroad.

_____ 3. Herbert Hoover believed that most of the help for the needy should come from
  a. charities.
  b. corporations.
  c. government.
  d. family and relatives.

_____ 4. Due largely to the voter frustration with Hoover, the congressional elections of 1930 were a victory for the
  a. Republican Party.
  b. Democratic Party.
  c. Socialist Party.
  d. Bull-Moose Party.

_____ 5. The Patman Bill called for an immediate bonus payment to
  a. artists.
  b. farmers.
  c. low-income families.
  d. World War I veterans.

_____ 6. The Bonus Army was dispersed by U.S. forces under the command of
  a. Douglas MacArthur.
  b. Dwight Eisenhower.
  c. Felix Frankfurter.
  d. John Pershing.

Name _____ Date _____

GEOGRAPHY APPLICATION: MOVEMENT
The Great Depression Takes Its Toll

Directions: Read the paragraphs below and study the map carefully. Then answer the questions that follow.

The effects of the Great Depression were heartbreaking. In 1932, for example, not a single person was employed in 28 percent of the families in the United States. Widespread unemployment contributed greatly to the steep 40 percent fall in average family income in the four years 1929–1933. In 1933 nearly 13 million workers, about 25 percent of the U.S. total, had no jobs.

Rates of unemployment, though, were far from uniform across the country. Some states—with industries such as radio and airplane production—were relatively well off, so that at one point, in 1934, there was a 33 percent difference between the highest and lowest state unemployment rates.

This disparity in unemployment rates started people moving all over the country. At the begin-

ning, many unemployed city dwellers moved to the countryside, hoping that farms were better off economically than cities. But soon agriculture suffered just as much as other businesses, especially during the Dust Bowl drought that began in 1933. Tens of thousands of families in the hardest-hit states—North Dakota, South Dakota, Nebraska, Kansas, Colorado, Oklahoma, and Texas—put everything they owned into cars and trucks and left home. (By 1936, some areas were ghostlike, with more than half of the houses abandoned.) By the end of the decade, all of the hardest-hit states except for Colorado and Texas had experienced population declines, even though the U.S. population grew by 9 million people during the decade.

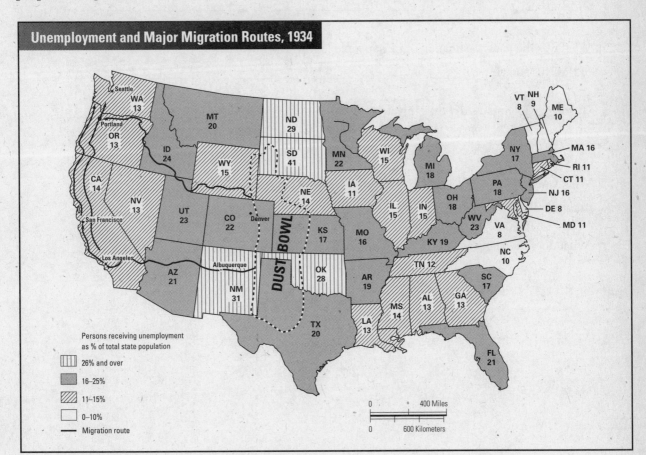

Unemployment and Major Migration Routes, 1934

Persons receiving unemployment as % of total state population

- 26% and over
- 16–25%
- 11–15%
- 0–10%
- Migration route

0   400 Miles
0   600 Kilometers

Interpreting Text and Visuals

1. Which four states had the highest unemployment rate in 1934?

   _____

   _____

2. Which region of the country—east or west of the Mississippi River—
   was better off in 1934? _____

   What statistics support your choice? _____

   _____

   _____

   _____

3. Which of the hardest-hit Dust Bowl states lost population in the 1930s?

   _____

   _____

4. What was the main destination of most people leaving the northern part
   of the Dust Bowl? _____

   Through which states did they travel? _____

   _____

5. What was the first destination of most people leaving the southern part
   of the Dust Bowl? _____

   What does the migration northward from Los Angeles imply? _____

   _____

   _____

   _____

CHAPTER

14

Section 1

PRIMARY SOURCE The Stock Market Crash

New York Times *reporter Elliott V. Bell witnessed firsthand the panic and despair that ensued after the stock market crashed on October 24, 1929. As you read his account, think about the chain of events that followed the crash.*

The market opened steady with prices little changed from the previous day, though some rather large blocks, of 20,000 to 25,000 shares, came out at the start. It sagged easily for the first half hour, and then around eleven o'clock the deluge broke.

It came with a speed and ferocity that left men dazed. The bottom simply fell out of the market. From all over the country a torrent of selling orders poured onto the floor of the Stock Exchange and there were no buying orders to meet it. Quotations of representative active issues, like Steel, Telephone, and Anaconda, began to fall two, three, five, and even ten points between sales. Less active stocks became unmarketable. Within a few moments the ticker service was hopelessly swamped and from then on no one knew what was really happening. By 1:30 the ticker tape was nearly two hours late; by 2:30 it was 147 minutes late. The last quotation was not printed on the tape until 7:08½ P.M., four hours, eight and one-half minutes after the close. In the meantime, Wall Street had lived through an incredible nightmare.

In the strange way that news of a disaster spreads, the word of the market collapse flashed through the city. By noon great crowds had gathered at the corner of Broad and Wall streets where the Stock Exchange on one corner faces Morgan's [the headquarters of J. P. Morgan] across the way. On the steps of the Sub-Treasury Building, opposite Morgan's, a crowd of press photographers and newsreel men took up their stand. Traffic was pushed from the streets of the financial district by the crush. . . .

The animal roar that rises from the floor of the Stock Exchange and which on active days is plainly audible in the Street outside, became louder, anguished, terrifying. The streets were crammed with a mixed crowd—agonized little speculators, walking aimlessly outdoors because they feared to face the ticker and the margin clerk; sold-out traders, morbidly impelled to visit the scene of their ruin; inquisitive individuals and tourists, seeking by gazing at the exteriors of the Exchange and the big banks to get a closer view of the national catastrophe; runners, frantically pushing their way through the throng of idle and curious in their effort to make deliveries of the unprecedented volume of securities which was being traded on the floor of the Exchange.

The ticker, hopelessly swamped, fell hours behind the actual trading and became completely meaningless. Far into the night, and often all night long, the lights blazed in the windows of the tall office buildings where margin clerks and bookkeepers struggled with the desperate task of trying to clear one day's business before the next began. They fainted at their desks; the weary runners fell exhausted on the marble floors of banks and slept. But within a few months they were to have ample time to rest up. By then thousands of them had been fired.

Agonizing scenes were enacted in the customers' rooms of the various brokers. There traders who a few short days before had luxuriated in delusions of wealth saw all their hopes smashed in a collapse so devastating, so far beyond their wildest fears, as to seem unreal. Seeking to save a little from the wreckage, they would order their stocks sold "at the market," in many cases to discover that they had not merely lost everything but were, in addition, in debt to the broker. And then, ironic twist, as like as not the next few hours' wild churning of the market would lift prices to levels where they might have sold out and had a substantial cash balance left over. Every move was wrong, in those days. The market seemed like an insensate thing that was wreaking a wild and pitiless revenge upon those who had thought to master it.

from H. W. Baldwin and Shepard Stone, eds., *We Saw It Happen* (New York: 1938). Reprinted in Richard B. Morris and James Woodress, eds., *Voices from America's Past*, vol. 3, The Twentieth Century (New York: Dutton, 1962), 90–94.

Research Options

1. Find out prices of several stocks, such as RCA or General Motors, after the October 1929 crash. Then look at the business section of today's newspaper to compare the 1929 prices with prices of the same stocks today.

2. On October 19, 1987, the stock market crashed again. Find out about Black Monday in 1987 and then discuss with classmates the similarities and differences between this crash and the crash of October 1929.

PRIMARY SOURCE Political Cartoon

CHAPTER
14
Section 1

This Pulitzer Prize–winning cartoon by John T. McCutcheon was published in the Chicago Tribune in 1931. Study the cartoon to find out who the "wise economist" is.

Activity Options

1. How do you think the Great Depression changed people's lives? Write a diary entry from the point of view of the man in this cartoon. Share your entry with classmates.

2. Draw an original cartoon to illustrate the impact of financial collapse following the stock market crash. Use the characters in this cartoon or invent your own. Display your cartoon in class.

PRIMARY SOURCE Letter from a Dust Bowl Survivor

The following letter was written by a survivor of the Dust Bowl in McCracken, Kansas. What problems does she attribute to the drought in the Great Plains?

March 24, 1935

Dear Family,

Did some of you think that you had a dust storm? I'll tell you what it was. It was us shaking our bedding, carpets, etc.

For over a week we have been having troublesome times. The dust is something fierce. Sometimes it lets up enough so we can see around; even the sun may shine for a little time, then we have a frenzied time of cleaning, anticipating the comfort of a clean feeling once more.

We keep the doors and windows all shut tight, with wet papers on the sills. The tiny particles of dirt sift right through the walls. Two different times it has been an inch thick on my kitchen floor.

Our faces look like coal miners', our hair is gray and stiff with dirt and we grind dirt in our teeth. We have to wash everything just before we eat it and make it as snappy as possible. Sometimes there is a fog all through the house and all we can do about it is sit on our dusty chairs and see that fog settle slowly and silently over everything.

When we open the door, swirling whirlwinds of soil beat against us unmercifully, and we are glad to go back inside and sit choking in the dirt. We couldn't see the streetlight just in front of the house.

One morning, early, I went out during a lull, and when I started to return I couldn't see the house. I knew the direction, so I kept on coming, and was quite close before I could even see the outline. It sure made me feel funny.

There has not been much school this week. It let up a little yesterday and Fred went with the janitor and they carried dirt out of the church by the scoopful. Four of them worked all afternoon. We were able to have church this morning, but I think many stayed home to clean.

A lot of dirt is blowing now, but it's not dangerous to be out in it. This dirt is all loose, any little wind will stir it, and there will be no relief until we get rain. If it doesn't come soon there will be lots of suffering. If we spit or blow our noses we get mud. We have quite a little trouble with our chests. I understand a good many have pneumonia.

As for gardens, we had ours plowed, but now we do not know whether we have more or less soil. It's useless to plant anything.

Grace

from Deb Mulvey, ed., *"We Had Everything but Money"* (Greendale, Wis.: Reiman, 1992), 43.

Discussion Questions

1. According to Grace's letter, what problems did people living in the Dust Bowl encounter?
2. How would you describe Grace's attitude about the dust?
3. What qualities or traits do you think helped Grace and her family survive the difficulties that they faced?

CHAPTER 14

Section 3

PRIMARY SOURCE Attack on the Bonus Army

The government planned to pay World War I veterans bonuses in 1945; however, in 1932 tens of thousands of veterans and their families descended on Washington to demand immediate payment. President Hoover eventually ordered the U.S. Army to drive the Bonus Army from the capital. As you read this excerpt from reporter Lee McCardell's eyewitness account, consider whether the veterans were treated fairly.

WASHINGTON, July 29—The bonus army was retreating today—in all directions. . . .

The fight had begun, as far as the Regular Army was concerned, late yesterday afternoon. The troops had been called out after a veteran of the Bonus Army had been shot and killed by a Washington policeman during a skirmish to drive members of the Bonus Army out of a vacant house on Pennsylvania Avenue, two blocks from the Capitol.

The soldiers numbered between seven hundred and eight hundred men. There was a squadron of the Third Cavalry from Fort Myer, a battalion of the Twelfth Infantry from Fort Washington, and a platoon of tanks (five) from Fort Meade. Most of the police in Washington seemed to be trailing after the soldiers, and traffic was tied up in 115 knots.

The cavalry clattered down Pennsylvania Avenue with drawn sabers.

The infantry came marching along with fixed bayonets.

All Washington smelled a fight, and all Washington turned out to see it.

Streets were jammed with automobiles.

Sidewalks, windows, doorsteps were crowded with people trying to see what was happening.

"Yellow! Yellow!"

From around the ramshackle shelters which they had built on a vacant lot fronting on Pennsylvania Avenue, just above the Capitol, the bedraggled veterans jeered. . . .

The cavalrymen stretched out in extended order and rode spectators back on the sidewalks. The infantry started across the lot, bayonets fixed.

Veterans in the rear ranks of a mob that faced the infantry pushed forward. Those in front pushed back. The crowd stuck. An order went down the line of infantrymen. The soldiers stepped back, pulled tear-gas bombs from their belts, and hurled them into the midst of the mob.

Some of the veterans grabbed the bombs and threw them back at the infantry. The exploding tins whizzed around the smooth asphalt like devil chasers, pfutt-pfutt-pfutt. And a gentle southerly wind wafted the gas in the faces of the soldiers and the spectators across the street.

Cavalrymen and infantrymen jerked gas masks out of their haversacks. The spectators, blinded and choking with the unexpected gas attack, broke and fled. Movie photographers who had parked their sound trucks so as to catch a panorama of the skirmish ground away doggedly, tears streaming down their faces.

The police tied handkerchiefs around their faces.

"Ya-a-a-ah!" jeered the veterans.

But more gas bombs fell behind them. The veterans were caught in the back draft. They began to retreat. But before they quit their shacks they set them on fire. The dry wood and rubbish from which the huts were fashioned burned quickly. The flames shot high. Clouds of dirty brown smoke blanketed the avenue.

from Lee McCardell, Baltimore *Evening Sun,* July 29, 1932. Reprinted in Richard B. Morris and James Woodress, eds., *Voices from America's Past,* vol. 3, The Twentieth Century (New York: Dutton, 1962), 94–97.

Discussion Questions

1. According to McCardell, what sparked the fight between Bonus Army veterans and the soldiers?
2. How did the soldiers drive the veterans from the capital?
3. Do you think the veterans were treated fairly? Why or why not? Cite evidence from your textbook to support your opinion.

CHAPTER 14

Section 2

LITERATURE SELECTION *from In the Beginning*
by Chaim Potok

In the Beginning, *set during the Great Depression and World War II, traces events in the lives of the Luries, a Jewish family living in the Bronx. As you read this excerpt from the novel, think about how the narrator, first-grader David Lurie, views the hardship and suffering caused by the Depression.*

They sat in the living room talking and I lay in my bed listening. I heard words in Yiddish and English that I did not understand. How could it happen? someone would say. Who could have foreseen it? There were those who predicted it, someone else would say. No one listened. What good is it to complain? my father would say. We have to think what to do. Tell us, they would say. What should we do? It's lost, a despairing voice would say. There is nothing to be done. That is not a helpful attitude, my aunt would say. But it's the truth, the despairing voice would say. There is nothing to be done. Nonsense, my father would say. We must stay together and we will plan what to do. They would talk back and forth in low voices. Sometimes a voice would suddenly be raised in anger. Once I heard a man cry out, "How long can I go on, Max? They are tearing pieces from me!" And they quieted and soothed him, and I heard my mother say she would bring him a glass of tea. Often there were sudden silences, dense chasms in the uneven contour of their speech, and I imagined I could hear the darkness of the night seeping into the room through the minute crevices in our windows. I thought often of the picnic in the clearing. When had that been? Before the summer? I could barely remember. I thought of the way my father had sounded the shofar on Rosh Hashanah, had prayed the Afternoon Service on Yom Kippur, had danced with the Torah on Simchat Torah. The joy of his friends, the ringing happiness that had filled the little synagogue. Now they sat as if it were the start of a war and they needed to make plans to flee from the Angel of Death. Had they met this way in Lemberg during the big war? I listened and was very tired and wished I could sleep. But sleep remained a cool and distant stranger. I wondered if there were some kind of special prayer one could offer for sleep. Mrs. Horowitz would have known. I stayed awake late into the nights, and slept and daydreamed in my classes during the days. My teachers left me alone.

All through the winter and into the spring those meetings continued. They brought strange dread into the house. With the coming of the warm weather, I began to have the feeling that my father and his friends were having all those meetings not so much for the purpose of making plans as for the simple need to be together and support one another, to drink glasses of tea in each other's homes, to offer one another words of encouragement, to keep away despair. I did not know what they feared, and I was afraid to ask. I lay awake in the night and listened to the meetings, or to Saul practicing his Torah reading, or to my parents talking very quietly in the kitchen and then listening to the radio—I lay awake and felt alone and filled with dread.

I was ill often in the spring, once with a raging fever that kept me in bed more than ten days. They met at our apartment during that time. One night I heard their voices distorted through fever; they seemed the cries of dark and fearful birds. The pain in my face and forehead was almost unendurable. The light stung my eyes. I slid down beneath my sheet and blanket. In the living room I heard my uncle's voice raised in a hoarse shout. There were loud, angry responses. I began to cry. The voices continued, subdued once again, a rushing, murmuring, voice-interrupting-voice multiple conversation of frightened people. I lay beneath my sheet and blanket, crying silently in pain and fever, waiting for the darkness to invade my impregnable sheet world.

It seemed to be everywhere, that darkness; and it grew darker still with the passing weeks. I was ill for the first two days of Passover. But I was in our synagogue for the final two days of the festival and it seemed a weary congregation. There were many empty seats. There was no picnic in the pine wood that June. On the final day of school I was told by my teachers that it had been decided to skip me an entire year. In September I would begin third grade.

I went gratefully to our cottage that summer

and had a restful time rowing and swimming and lying in the sun. My father and uncle were rarely with us the first three weeks. They remained in the city and came up for the weekends.

Then in August, my father abruptly stopped going to the city. "There is nothing happening in the city," I heard him tell my mother early one morning in the last week of July. "The city is like a cemetery. Its dead sell apples instead of lying still. It depresses me. Who needs a real estate broker now? I will stay here for August."

He would wake late and come out of the cottage unshaven and stare across the beach at the sun on the lake. He would sit hunched forward on a wicker chair in the shade of the elm and stare down at the grass, his veined muscular arms dangling loosely between his thighs. He grew silent. I feared going near him. His dark eyes burned fiercely and his square bony face seemed a block of carved stone. Long into the nights I would hear my mother talking to him, softly, imploringly. It seemed she did most of the talking now; he was silent.

One Shabbat afternoon he went into the forest and was gone so long that my mother grew afraid. She was about to ask my uncle to search for him when he emerged from its bluish depths and, without a word, went into the cottage. I saw my aunt and uncle look at each other forlornly. My mother went inside and came back out a few moments later and sat down in the wicker chair. She tried reading one of the German storybooks she had brought with her that summer, but in the end she put it aside and sat gazing at the afternoon sun on the lake. After a while she rose and returned to the cottage and did not come out until it was time to call Alex and me in for supper.

Far into the night my mother and father and aunt and uncle sat on our screened-in front porch and talked. I lay awake and listened but they were speaking in such subdued tones that I could make out nothing of what they were saying. On occasion one of their voices would rise above the surface of their conversation, but the others would immediately make mention of the children, and the loud voice would sink into a level of sound inaudible to my ears. I was at my window when they left and I saw my uncle embrace my father. He held him in the embrace for what seemed to me to be a very

Far into the night my mother and father and aunt and uncle sat on our screened-in front porch and talked.

long time while my mother and aunt looked on and, finally, looked away. Then my aunt and uncle went to their cottage and my parents went to bed.

But they did not sleep. Through the darkness and the thin wall that separated our bedrooms, I heard whispers and my mother's soothing words and my father's strained, subdued voice. "I cannot understand it, Ruth. There is nothing we can do. I have never been in a situation like this before. In Lemberg [a city in Poland] we could do something and see results. Why did I bring them here?"

"You did nothing wrong, Max. You advised them. That was all you did."

"But I told them it would be better here. Do you see how some of them look at me? I feel like a criminal."

"It isn't only here, Max. It's the whole world. Is it better where they were?"

"But I brought them *here*, Ruth. I worked like a slave—to bring them *here*. Now it is a catastrophe and nothing we can do will help. God in heaven, what have I done to my friends?"

And there were more whispers and it all went on a long time until I fell asleep numb with weariness and dread.

My father did not go horseback riding that summer, though he took us often to the movies. Sometimes he went to the movies alone, and I knew it was a war film. We returned to the city in the first week of September, and my father and uncle sold the cottages and we never saw them again.

The meetings continued, less frequently now but with greater rancor than before. Often I heard the gentle voice of my uncle raised in defense of my father. Who hadn't put money into the market? he would shout. Who hadn't invested in real estate? They were lucky he had pulled out as much as he had or there would be no money now to maintain the cemetery, to keep up the death benefits, to maintain the sick fund. No, there was no money for travel loans to get families from Europe to America. Not now. Not until times were better. But what were they complaining about? Why were they shouting at Max? Didn't they read the newspapers? People were jumping out of windows. At least there was still enough money in the treasury to keep the Am Kedoshim Society from bankruptcy.

I would lie in my bed and listen to his voice and imagine his gentle face red with anger, his eyes flaring behind their lenses. and I would remember how he had once said to me, "What should we have done, David? Sometimes you have to smash." His voice had been soft then, but I thought I could remember some of the anger that had been embedded within it. His eyes had flashed for the briefest of seconds; the face had gone rigid. It was strange how a gentle person could turn so suddenly raging.

There were more empty seats in the synagogue now; people were moving from the neighborhood. Often on my way to meet Saul on the boulevard where we waited for our trolley car, I would see moving vans parked on the curb and brawny men carrying furniture out of houses.

"Why are so many people moving, Saul?" I asked him one morning when we had taken seats in the trolley car.

"They can't pay the high rent. They move to a less expensive neighborhood."

"Will we have to move, Saul?"

"No, we won't have to move, Davey.". . .

Saul hunched his thin shoulders and pulled his heavy jacket more tightly around him. It was cold in the trolley car. People rode in silence, reading newspapers or staring at the slatted floor or out the windows at the gray morning. I gazed out my window a moment, then opened my Chumash and reviewed some passages on which we were to be tested that morning. I closed the Chumash and went over the passages again inside my eyes. Then I sat looking out the window.

I counted four moving vans that morning parked along the streets, their backs open like black mouths. One morning in January, as the trolley car turned into the street beyond the small park, I saw men moving furniture onto the sidewalk and leave it there. I did not see any moving van. The next day, Yaakov Bader came over to me during the mid-morning recess and said, "Come on and have a game with us, Davey."

I shrugged and continued looking through the chain-link fence at the street.

"Come on, Davey. My uncle told me to make sure and take good care of you. I don't want my uncle to be angry at me."

I turned to him. A red wool cap framed his fair-skinned features which were flushed pink by the cold.

He led me to a sheltered corner of the yards where, in a basement doorway beneath the outdoor fire stairs, I joined a game of baseball cards. The boys played with their gloves off. They blew into their hands and stamped their feet. I played seriously against the background noise of the recess and lost all my cards.

"Boy, Davey, you may be a big brain, but you're lousy at this. Look at all these Babe Ruths," one of them said.

"You ought to take your gloves off when you play, Davey," another said.

"It hurts my fingers to do that."

"Look at these hands," a third said. He thrust a pair of chapped and reddened hands in front of my eyes. "My mother will kill me.What did I spend money on gloves for if you don't wear them? She'll absolutely kill me. How can you play with gloves on, Davey?"

I shrugged and moved away from them. Yaakov Bader walked with me through the noisy yard back to the chain-link fence.

"They were only kidding you, Davey. Don't be so serious." We looked out at the deserted winter street.

"Is your uncle still in Europe?" I asked.

"He'll be there until the summer."

"What does he do?"

"He's living in Switzerland this year."

"Is he still in business?"

"Yes."

"So many people went out of business. My father doesn't have much business now. He's home a lot."

We were quiet, staring through the fence at the street.

"And so many people are moving. One of the boys in my house moved the other day. Monday, I think it was. Joey Younger. He's in second grade. Do you know him?"

He shook his head.

"I never liked him too much. But I was sorry he had to move."

Activity Option

1. Role-play a conversation in which Max and Ruth Lurie explain to their son David what is happening to the nation's economy and how this economic situation affects their lives.

CHAPTER 14

Section 1

AMERICAN LIVES Gordon Parks

Humane Artist

"I hope always to feel the responsibility to communicate the plight of others less fortunate than myself. . . . In helping one another we can ultimately save ourselves. We must give up silent watching and put our commitments into practice."—Gordon Parks, Moments Without Proper Names (1975)

Gordon Parks is an artist who has pursued art wherever he finds it. He has taken photographs, written poetry, composed music, and made films. Through it all, he has tried to convey his understanding of the human condition.

Born in 1912 as the last of fifteen children on a Kansas farm, Parks left school as a teenager to work. He held many different jobs—from busing tables to playing the piano to writing songs. Though it was the Depression, some people still had wealth. Parks earned a decent living as a waiter serving meals in a private men's club and on a cross-country train that carried wealthy passengers. One day, he saw a magazine with striking photographs, and it aroused an interest in photography. That interest was confirmed some months later when he heard a newsreel cameraman describe his exciting life. Parks bought a used camera and began taking pictures.

Settling in Chicago, he earned a living taking fashion photographs and photo portraits of women in society. At the same time, he shot documentary pictures of African-American life in the city. These pictures earned him a fellowship that led him to Washington. After a 10-year-period working for the federal government and again taking fashion pictures, he landed a plum assignment for photographers. Beginning in 1948, he began a 20-year career taking pictures around the world for *Life* magazine.

Parks lived for some years in Paris and at other times in Rio de Janeiro. He began taking fashion photos in Paris but soon branched into other areas. He took photo portraits of famous people. Most important, perhaps, were his images of social significance. He spent some months in the slums of Rio de Janeiro, capturing the difficult life of the poor. One young boy he met was dying of asthma. Parks's pictures of him deeply touched *Life* readers. They gave thousands of dollars, which he used to bring the boy to the United States for medical care that saved his life. Another series of photos chronicled the progress of the civil rights movement. Parks became the first African-American photojournalist.

Soon Parks was branching into other arts. He wrote a novel called *The Learning Tree*, which put in fictional terms the story of his childhood. He published four books of poetry and photographs. Later he wrote three volumes of memoirs.

He became the first African-American director of a major movie with a film version of *The Learning Tree* in 1969. He was also producer, screenwriter, and composer of the score for the film. Critics found the film visually stunning but too melodramatic. It did not attract a large audience— but his next movie, *Shaft* (1971), did. This classic detective story—featuring an African-American detective—was a great hit. Parks directed several other films. *Leadbelly* (1976) told the story of blues musician Huddie Ledbetter. *The Odyssey of Solomon Northrup* (1983) was a public-television drama about a free black sold into slavery. He also directed several documentaries for television, including one that won an award.

Parks has continued his range of artistic interest. He worked as editorial director of *Essence* magazine from 1970 to 1973. In 1989 he composed a ballet, *Martin*, which pays tribute to Dr. Martin Luther King, Jr. For accomplishments, such as this, Parks has received many awards and honors, including the National Medal of Arts in 1988. However, perhaps the highest compliment was paid to him in 1995 when the Library of Congress sought and acquired Parks's archives—thousands of photographs and around 15,000 manuscript pages of screenplays, novels, and poems.

Questions

1. How has Parks used his art to "communicate the plight of others"?
2. How would Parks's varied jobs help him in his career as a photographer?
3. In which arts did Parks achieve the greatest success?

CHAPTER 14

Section 1

AMERICAN LIVES **Alfred E. Smith**
The "Happy Warrior"

"I have taken an oath of office nineteen times. Each time I swore to defend and maintain the Constitution of the United States. . . . I have never known any conflict between my official duties and my religious beliefs."—Alfred E. Smith, "Catholic and Patriot" (1927)

Alfred E. Smith (1873–1944) was born and raised in New York's Lower East Side. His grandparents on one side had emigrated from Germany and Italy and on the other side from Ireland. He became identified with the rising power of urban immigrant voters.

Smith's father died when Alfred was twelve, and two years later, he quit school and began working full time. In the late 1890s, he entered local politics, and by 1903 he had won a seat in the New York state assembly. Dominating New York City politics was the Tammany Hall machine, and Smith was part of that Democratic party organization. He avoided any hint of corruption, however, and became known as an honest lawmaker. While working to achieve Tammany goals, he also pushed for various reforms.

In 1913, fire destroyed the Triangle garment factory, killing 146 people—mostly working women and girls. Smith led the outcry for greater workplace safety. He chaired a commission that investigated factory conditions throughout the state. The investigation put him in touch with many social reformers. These allies helped him in his 1918 race for governor. Smith campaigned for government reform and changes in female and child labor laws. He won a narrow victory.

As governor, Smith steered an independent course. He appointed Republicans and independents to state office. He backed labor's right to organize but used the state militia to end a violent strike. In the midst of widespread fear of radicals, he boldly criticized the New York assembly for expelling five members because they were socialists. He lost the governorship in 1920, although he won again in 1922, 1924, and 1926. In his later terms, he achieved many reform goals.

Smith tried to win the Democratic nomination for president in 1924. Franklin Delano Roosevelt nominated him, calling him the "Happy Warrior." Smith was anything but happy as the convention unfolded. The Ku Klux Klan—powerful in the party that year—opposed him loudly because he was a Roman Catholic. Finally Smith was forced to withdraw his candidacy.

Four years later, though, Smith easily won the nomination, but he entered the fall campaign with three problems. He was identified as a "wet"—someone against Prohibition—at a time when Prohibition still had wide support. He was Catholic, and no Catholic had ever run for president. And the country had prospered under eight years of Republican presidents.

Smith took the religious issue head-on. He gave a major speech in Oklahoma City urging tolerance of all religions. Some groups strongly opposed to him used harsh language. One critic linked Smith to a catalog of problems: "card playing, cocktail drinking, poodle dogs, divorces, novels, stuffy rooms, dancing, [and] evolution." Some Klan members said that to vote for Smith was to "vote for the Pope." Smith, however, pulled more votes than any previous Democratic candidate. He won two states and twelve large cities that had been solidly Republican. However, Smith lost by a wide margin.

Smith hoped to get a job working for Franklin Roosevelt, the new governor of New York. FDR did not name him to any post, however, and Smith entered business. Gradually he withdrew from politics. When he did enter political debates, he took more and more conservative positions. He harshly criticized Roosevelt in the early years of the New Deal. Not until World War II erupted did the two former allies become close again. Smith died in 1944.

Questions

1. How did Smith show independence throughout his career?
2. Why was Smith's Catholicism a major issue?
3. What problems besides opposition toward Catholicism helped defeat Smith?

CHAPTER
15
Section 1

GUIDED READING *A New Deal Fights the Depression*

A. As you read about President Roosevelt's New Deal, take notes to answer questions about each new federal program. The first one is done for you.

Federal Program	What was its immediate purpose?	What was its long-term goal?
Business Assistance and Reform 1. Emergency Banking Relief Act (EBRA)	*Authorized the Treasury Department to inspect and close banks*	*To restore public confidence in banks*
2. Glass-Steagall Banking Act of 1933		
3. Federal Securities Act		
4. National Industrial Recovery Act (NIRA)		
Farm Relief/Rural Development 5. Agricultural Adjustment Act (AAA)		
6. Tennessee Valley Authority (TVA)		
Employment Projects 7. Civilian Conservation Corps (CCC)		
8. Federal Emergency Relief Administration (FERA)		
9. Public Works Administration (PWA)		
10. Civil Works Administration (CWA)		
Housing 11. Home Owners Loan Corporation (HOLC)		

B. On the back of this paper, explain who **Huey Long** was and why he is a significant historical figure.

Name _____ Date _____

A. As you read this section, take notes to answer questions about the second phase of Roosevelt's New Deal policies.

Group	What problems did each group face during the Depression?	What laws were passed and agencies established to deal with these problems?
1. Farmers, migrant workers, and others living in rural areas		
2. Students and other young people		
3. Teachers, writers, artists, and other professionals		
4. All workers, including the unemployed		
5. Retired workers		
6. The disabled, the needy elderly, and dependent mothers and children		

B. On the back of this paper, describe how **Eleanor Roosevelt** contributed to the nation's recovery from the Depression.

CHAPTER 15

Section 3

GUIDED READING *The New Deal Affects Many Groups*

A. As you read, write notes about each group in Roosevelt's New Deal coalition.

1. Women Example(s) of appointees to important government positions:	Gains women made under the New Deal:	Problems of women not solved by the New Deal:

2. African Americans Example(s) of appointees to important government positions:	Gains African Americans made under the New Deal:	Problems of African Americans not solved by the New Deal:

3. Labor unions Example(s) of union(s) organized during the New Deal:	Gains unions made under the New Deal:	Problems of unions not solved by the New Deal:

4. Other coalition groups Other groups:	Reasons they supported the Democratic party:

B. On the back of this paper, explain who **John Collier** was and how he helped one of the New Deal coalition groups.

Name _____ Date _____

CHAPTER 15

Section 4

GUIDED READING *Culture of the 1930s*

As you read about how the Depression and New Deal influenced American culture, write notes in the appropriate boxes to answer the questions about each work.

Films and Radio Drama		
1. *Gone with the Wind*	What was it? Who created or appeared in it?	What was its theme?
2. *Mr. Smith Goes to Washington*	What was it? Who created or appeared in it?	What was its theme?
3. *The War of the Worlds*	What was it? Who created or appeared in it?	What was its theme?
4. *Waiting for Lefty*	What was it? Who created or appeared in it?	What was its theme?
Art and Literature		
5. *Native Son*	What was it? Who created or appeared in it?	What was its theme?
6. *The Grapes of Wrath*	What was it? Who created or appeared in it?	What was its theme?
7 *Our Town*	What was it? Who created or appeared in it?	What was its theme?
8. *American Gothic*	What was it? Who created or appeared in it?	What was its theme?

CHAPTER
15
Section 5

GUIDED READING *The Impact of the New Deal*

A. As you read about the impact of New Deal reforms, take notes about the lasting effects of those reforms on American society.

	New Deal Laws and Agencies	Lasting Effects of These Laws and Agencies on American Government and Life
1. Labor		
2. Agriculture and rural life		
3. Banking and finance		
4. Social welfare		
5. Environment		

B. On the back of this paper, explain the meaning of **parity.**

CHAPTER 15 BUILDING VOCABULARY *The New Deal*

A. Multiple Choice Circle the letter before the term or name that best completes the sentence.

1. The Glass-Steagall Act established the (a) Securities and Exchange Commission (b) Federal Deposit Insurance Corporation (c) Civilian Conservation Corps.

2. The Civil Works Administration provided money to states to create jobs mainly in the construction of (a) schools and other community buildings (b) dams and roads (c) historic monuments.

3. The Works Progress Administration was headed by (a) Eleanor Roosevelt (b) Huey Long (c) Harry Hopkins.

4. Frances Perkins was the nation's first (a) female cabinet member (b) African-American cabinet member (c) African-American to perform at the Lincoln Memorial.

5. The novel that depicts the arduous journey of Oklahoma farmers fleeing the Dust Bowl is (a) *Native Son* (b) *The Disinherited* (c) *The Grapes of Wrath*.

B. Matching Match the description in the second column with the term or name in the first column. Write the appropriate letter next to the word.

_____ 1. Civilian Conservation Corps   a. Roosevelt's program to fight the Depression

_____ 2. Richard Wright   b. measure that strengthened labor unions

_____ 3. deficit spending   c. famous Depression-era movie

_____ 4. New Deal   d. opponent of New Deal

_____ 5. *Gone With the Wind*   e. brought power to an impoverished region

_____ 6. Wagner Act   f. author of *Native Son*

_____ 7. Tennessee Valley Authority   g. put millions of young men to work

_____ 8. Huey Long   h. government spending that exceeds intake

C. Writing Write a paragraph about how the New Deal affected the nation's minorities. Use the following names and terms.

Mary McLeod Bethune   **John Collier**   **New Deal Coalition**

CHAPTER 15

Section 1

SKILLBUILDER PRACTICE *Analyzing Issues*

In 1996, the issue of individual rights versus government protection became prominent as ever-expanding communications technology raised the question of how to protect children from undesirable material on the Internet. Read the description of some of the arguments, then fill in the chart to analyze this issue. (See Skillbuilder Handbook, p. R14.)

The Communications Decency Act As part of a widely supported effort to protect children from access to obscenity and other inappropriate materials on the Internet, Congress passed the Communications Decency Act of 1996, making it a crime to knowingly transmit certain kinds of materials to children over the Internet. President Clinton hailed the action as government helping parents protect their children. Certain parent organizations also applauded the law.

Some advocates of the act pointed out that American taxpayers had helped finance development of the Internet as the federal government worked to build the early stages of the web. It follows, then, these advocates said, that all Americans—no matter what their age, interests, or values may be—should be able to use the Internet without being offended by material they encounter.

A Violation of Free Speech Opponents of the act, including the American Civil Liberties Union and the American Library Association, proclaimed that it violated First Amendment rights of

free speech. They agreed that children's access to certain materials on the Internet should be supervised, but they believed that parents and schools, not the government, should be responsible for that supervision. They recommended a number of software filters on the market that parents could buy to screen Internet content in their own home.

Opponents also pointed out that the Internet contains vast amounts of information, and only a small portion falls into the category of being obscene or otherwise inappropriate for children. Furthermore, they said, it is highly unlikely that children would actually stumble upon these sites as they "surfed the Net," and most such sites already begin with warnings to children.

In June 1996, a federal court in Philadelphia reviewed the Communications Decency Act and found it to be unconstitutional. The judges unanimously agreed that the Internet should be protected from government interference. Proponents of the act appealed the case to the U.S. Supreme Court, where all sides of the issue would be examined again.

The issue:

The response: Passage of the Communications Decency Act

PROPONENTS

Who they are:

Their arguments:

OPPONENTS

Who they are:

Their arguments:

CHAPTER
15

Section 1

RETEACHING ACTIVITY *A New Deal Fights*
the Depression

Matching

A. Complete each sentence with the appropriate term or name.

kitchen cabinet   National Industrial Recovery Act
fireside chats   Federal Securities Act
Civilian Conservation Corps   "Brain Trust"
nationalization   executive privilege
separation of powers   National Recovery Administration

1. The group of advisers whom Roosevelt assembled to help him devise his New Deal policies were
   known as the _____.

2. Roosevelt tried to allay the country's fears about the Depression through a series of radio
   conversations known as _____.

3. The _____ was a New Deal program that set prices of many products to ensure fair
   competition.

4. Critics believed that Roosevelt's "court-packing" bill violated the notion of _____.

5. New Deal critic Charles Coughlin favored a guaranteed income and the _____ of banks.

Evaluating

B. Write *T* in the blank if the statement is true. If the statement is false, write *F* in the
blank and then write the corrected statement on the line below.

_____ 1. The three main goals of the New Deal were relief for the needy, economic recovery, and
increased speculation.

_____

_____ 2. The period of intense economic activity in which Congress passed numerous New Deal
measures was known as the Hundred Days.

_____

_____ 3. One action taken by the Civilian Conservation Corps was to replant trees on the Great
Plains to help prevent another Dust Bowl.

_____

_____ 4. The Twenty-second Amendment, passed in 1933, repealed Prohibition.

_____

_____ 5. New Deal critic Dr. Francis Townsend argued that the Roosevelt Administration wasn't
doing enough to help the business community.

_____

Name _____ Date _____

RETEACHING ACTIVITY *The Second New Deal
Takes Hold*

Finding Main Ideas

The following questions deal with the Second New Deal. Answer them in the space provided.

1. What was significant about the presidential election of 1936?

_____

_____

2. How did the Second New Deal attempt to help farmers?

_____

_____

3. What types of work did participants in the Works Progress Administration undertake?

_____

_____

4. What did the Fair Labor Standards Act accomplish?

_____

_____

5. What groups did the Social Security Act seek to help?

_____

_____

6. How did the Wagner Act aid organized labor?

_____

_____

CHAPTER 15

Section 3

RETEACHING ACTIVITY   *The New Deal Affects Many Groups*

Multiple Choice

Choose the best answer for each item. Write the letter of your answer in the blank.

_____ 1. The country's first all-black trade union was organized by
   a. Mary McLeod Bethune.
   b. A. Philip Randolph.
   c. Frances Perkins.
   d. Robert C. Weaver.

_____ 2. Roosevelt did not do more to promote civil rights out of fear of upsetting
   a. Congress.
   b. westerners.
   c. labor unions.
   d. Southern Democrats.

_____ 3. Between 1933 and 1941, union membership in the United States grew from less
   than 3 million to about
   a. 5 million.
   b. 10 million.
   c. 12 million.
   d. 15 million.

_____ 4. One of the main bargaining tactics of the labor movement in the 1930s was the
   a. sit-down strike.
   b. work slowdown.
   c. boycott.
   d. walk-out.

_____ 5. The Memorial Day Massacre involved violent clashes between police and workers in the
   a. steel industry.
   b. oil industry.
   c. railroad industry.
   d. textile industry.

_____ 6. Frances Perkins became the first female
   a. federal judge.
   b. vice-president.
   c. cabinet member.
   d. presidential candidate.

CHAPTER 15

Section 4

RETEACHING ACTIVITY *Culture of the 1930s*

Matching

A. Match the description in the second column with the person or work in the first column. Write the appropriate letter next to the word.

_____ 1. Woodie Guthrie

_____ 2. *Gone with the Wind*

_____ 3. Richard Wright

_____ 4. *Grapes of Wrath*

_____ 5. Orson Welles

_____ 6. Grant Wood

a. depicted difficulties of Dust Bowl farmers

b. folksinger who captured daily hardships

c. created "The War of the Worlds" radio show

d. creator of famous painting *American Gothic*

e. famous Depression-era film

f. author of *Native Son*

Finding Main Ideas

B. The following questions deal wiith American culture during the Depression. Write your answers in the space provided.

1. How did the Federal Art Project help Depression-era artists?

_____

_____

2. Why did so many people regularly attend movies during the 1930s?

_____

_____

3. How did the art and literature of the Depression differ from the movie and radio productions of the time?

_____

_____

CHAPTER
15
Section 5

RETEACHING ACTIVITY *The Impact of the New Deal*

Completion

A. Complete each sentence with the appropriate term or name.

banking industry   stock market
social security   Federal Securities Act
deficit   World War II
Glass-Steagall Act   surplus

1. The Security and Exchange Commission today continues to regulate the _____.

2. After reaching retirement age, most Americans today receive _____ payments

3. With so much government spending, the New Deal helped to increase the federal _____.

4. The Federal Deposit Insurance Corporation was created by the _____.

5. What really ended the Great Depression was the increased spending and work opportunities brought on by _____.

Summarizing

B. Complete the chart below by summarizing the main arguments posed by critics and supporters of the New Deal.

Impact of the New Deal	
Supporters	**Critics**

CHAPTER 15

Section 5

GEOGRAPHY APPLICATION: REGION

Decade of the Democrats

Directions: Read the paragraphs below and study the maps carefully. Then answer the questions that follow.

The Democratic Party controlled the federal government for most of the 1930s. The Republicans' mostly voluntary programs to remedy the ravages of the Great Depression had failed, so in 1932 Democrat Franklin D. Roosevelt was elected president. Only the Northeast, a Republican stronghold, did not endorse Roosevelt. Elsewhere, his support was overwhelming.

The Democrats had put together a new coalition of voters: urban immigrants, blue-collar workers of the industrialized North, African Americans, farmers of the Midwest and Great Plains and citizens in the "Solid South" joined to give the Democratic Party a national majority for the first time since the Civil War.

These people had voted for change, and they got what they wanted. To put the nation on the road to economic recovery, Roosevelt pushed through a collection of work programs, often called "alphabet soup" for initials such as WPA and CCC. The mid-1930s marked the high point of these New Deal programs. Millions of people were put back to work, and many economic-recovery projects were in full swing.

By the end of the 1930s, however, the situation had changed. The country, slowly climbing out of the depths of the Great Depression, had suffered another period of economic decline in 1937–1938, and unemployment was once again a major problem. Business leaders and Congress had become more vocal in their criticism of the New Deal, and many of its programs were ended. By the 1940 presidential election, eight states—all in the agricultural Midwest and Great Plains—had switched their support from Roosevelt to the Republican candidate, Wendell Willkie. Though Roosevelt's popularity remained strong elsewhere, particularly in the Democratic stronghold of the South, it would take the U.S. involvement in World War II to jolt the nation's economy into the full recovery that Roosevelt had been seeking.

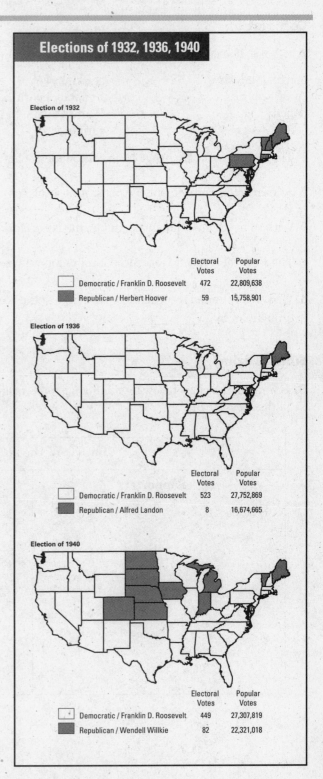

Elections of 1932, 1936, 1940

Election of 1932

		Electoral Votes	Popular Votes
☐	Democratic / Franklin D. Roosevelt	472	22,809,638
■	Republican / Herbert Hoover	59	15,758,901

Election of 1936

		Electoral Votes	Popular Votes
☐	Democratic / Franklin D. Roosevelt	523	27,752,869
■	Republican / Alfred Landon	8	16,674,665

Election of 1940

		Electoral Votes	Popular Votes
☐	Democratic / Franklin D. Roosevelt	449	27,307,819
■	Republican / Wendell Willkie	82	22,321,018

Interpreting Text and Visuals

1. Which part of the country failed to support Franklin D. Roosevelt in the 1932 presidential election? _____

2. Which states remained Republican in all three elections? (You may consult the atlas, pp. A1–A21, for the names of U.S. states.) _____

   What regions of the United States remained solidly Democratic in all three elections? _____

   _____

3. The 1936 election is a good example of the frequent disparity between popular and electoral totals. Roosevelt received more than 65 times as many electoral votes as Landon. But was the popular vote for Roosevelt about 90 times as great, 9 times as great, or 1.5 times as great as that for Landon?

   _____

4. Compare Roosevelt's victory in 1940 with his victory in 1936. In what respect did he lose ground? _____

   _____

   _____

   _____

5. In which election did the Democratic Party achieve its greatest popularity? _____

6. What do you think was the main cause of Herbert Hoover's loss in 1932? _____

   _____

   _____

7. What trend do you notice in the Democratic vote in the 1940 election? _____

   _____

   _____

   _____

   _____

Name _____ Date _____

CHAPTER
15
Section 5

OUTLINE MAP *Anatomy of the Tennessee Valley Authority*

A. Review the map of the Tennessee Valley Authority (TVA) on textbook pages 520–521. Then, on the accompanying map, locate the same 11 states found on the textbook map and add the following bodies of water, cities, and dams.

Bodies of Water	Cities	Dams
Cumberland R.	Chattanooga	Chickamauga Dam
Kentucky Lake	Knoxville	Fort Loudoun Dam
Mississippi R.	Memphis	Guntersville Dam
Ohio R.	Nashville	Kentucky Dam
Tennessee R.	Paducah	Nickajack Dam

B. After completing the map, use it to answer the following questions.

1. Use the scale bar to estimate both the east–west and north–south distances of the area served by the TVA. _____

2. Which states does the TVA serve? _____

_____

_____

3. The Tennessee River begins at Knoxville. Which is the first dam on the river? the last dam? the southernmost? _____

_____

_____

4. Which is the first dam encountered after Chattanooga? _____

5. How many dams does the Tennessee River have? _____

6. Describe the journey that a molecule of water at the Tennessee River's source takes to reach Memphis. _____

_____

_____

_____

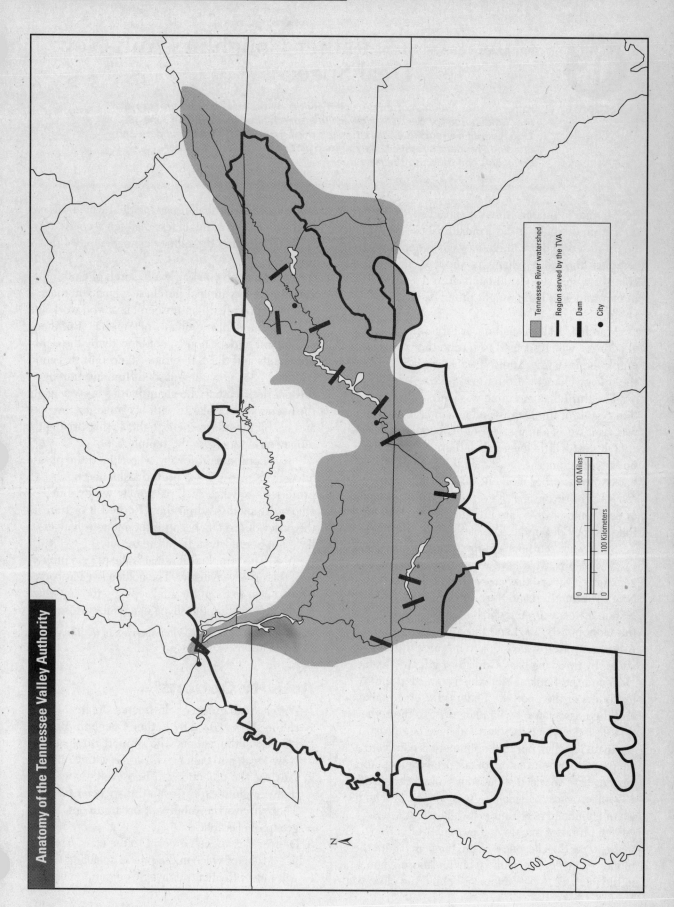

Anatomy of the Tennessee Valley Authority

| Tennessee River watershed |
| Region served by the TVA |
| Dam |
| City |

100 Miles

100 Kilometers

N

CHAPTER 15

Section 1

PRIMARY SOURCE *from* Father Coughlin's Anti-New Deal Speech

Father Charles Coughlin often discussed politics on his weekly radio broadcast, the "Golden Hour of the Little Flower." In a speech aired on WABC on June 19, 1936, Coughlin endorsed William Lemke's third-party presidential candidacy and attacked President Roosevelt. As you read part of this speech, consider Coughlin's opposition to the New Deal.

No man in modern times received such plaudits from the poor as did Franklin Roosevelt when he promised to drive the money changers from the temple—the money changers who had clipped the coins of wages, who had manufactured spurious money and who had brought proud America to her knees.

March 4, 1933! I shall never forget the inaugural address, which seemed to reecho the very words employed by Christ Himself as He actually drove the money changers from the temple.

The thrill that was mine was yours. Through dim clouds of the Depression this man Roosevelt was, as it were, a new savior of his people!

Oh, just a little longer shall there be needless poverty! Just another year shall there be naked backs! Just another moment shall there be dark thoughts of revolution! Never again will the chains of economic poverty bite into the hearts of simple folks as they did in the past days of the Old Deal!

Such were our hopes in the springtime of 1933.

My friends, what have we witnessed as the finger of time turned the pages of the calendar? Nineteen hundred and thirty-three and the National Recovery Act which multiplied profits for the monopolists; 1934 and the AAA [Agricultural Adjustment Act] which raised the price of foodstuffs, by throwing back God's best gifts in His face; 1935 and the Banking Act which rewarded the exploiters of the poor, the Federal Reserve bankers and their associates, by handing over to them the temple from which they were to have been cast!

In 1936, when our disillusionment is complete, we pause to take inventory of our predicament. You citizens have shackled about your limbs a tax bill of $35 billion, most of which . . . was created by a flourish of a fountain pen. Your erstwhile savior, whose golden promises ring upon the counter of performance with the cheapness of tin, bargained with the money changers that, with 70 billion laboring hours in the ditch, or in the factory, or behind the plow, you

and your children shall repay the debt which was created with a drop of ink in less than ten seconds.

Is that driving the money changers out of the temple?

Every crumb you eat, every stitch of clothing you wear, every menial purchase which you make is weighted down with an unseen tax as you work and slave for the debt merchants of America. But the $55 billion of debt bonds, held mostly by the debt merchants and the well-circumstanced of this country, have been ably safeguarded from taxation by this peerless leader who sham-battles his way along the avenue of popularity with his smile for the poor and his blindness for their plight. Is that driving the money changers from the temple? . . .

It is not pleasant for me who coined the phrase "Roosevelt or ruin" —a phrase fashioned upon promises—to voice such passionate words. But I am constrained to admit that "Roosevelt or ruin" is the order of the day because the money changers have not been driven from the temple. . . .

Alas! The temple still remains the private property of the money changers. The golden key has been handed over to them for safekeeping—the key which is now fashioned in the shape of a double cross.

from Charles E. Coughlin, *Vital Speeches of the Day,* July 1, 1936, 613–616.

Activity Options

1. With a small group of classmates, create a radio call-in show hosted by Father Coughlin. Role-play Coughlin, callers who support Roosevelt's New Deal, and callers who agree with Coughlin.
2. Analyze the objections to Roosevelt's New Deal that Coughlin expresses in this speech excerpt. Then discuss the validity of his arguments with a group of classmates.
3. Deliver this speech excerpt to the class. Try to use a tone of voice and a rate of speaking that will most effectively convey Coughlin's message.

CHAPTER 15

Section 3

PRIMARY SOURCE The Memorial Day Massacre

On Memorial Day in 1937, the Chicago police attacked a picket line of striking Republic Steel Company workers and their families. As you read this New York Times *report about the incident, think about why this demonstration turned violent.*

CHICAGO, May 30—Four men were killed and eighty-four persons went to hospitals with gunshot wounds, cracked heads, broken limbs, or other injuries received in a battle late this afternoon between police and steel strikers at the gates of the Republic Steel Corporation plant in South Chicago.

The clash occurred when about one thousand strikers tried to approach the Republic company's plant, the only mill of the three large independent steel manufacturers in this area attempting to continue production. About 22,000 steelworkers are on strike in the Chicago district.

The union demonstrators were armed with clubs, slingshots, cranks and gearshift levers from cars, bricks, steel bolts, and other missiles. Police charged that some of the men also carried firearms.

The riot grew out of a meeting held by steel-mill workers in protest against the action of police, who turned them back Friday night when they attempted to approach the Republic plant.

The march was organized at this meeting, held outside CIO headquarters at One Hundred and Thirteenth Street and Green Bay Avenue, three blocks from the plant. The strikers said they were going to march through the main-gate entrance in an effort to force closing of the mill.

Heading the march were strikers from the Youngstown Sheet and Tube Company and Inland Steel Company plants in the Calumet district. They had been invited to the mass meeting and had volunteered to lead the march on the Republic, where about 1400 workers were said to be still on the job.

The union men chose a time when the police were changing shifts, hoping, the police said, to catch them disorganized. But Captain James L. Mooney, Captain Thomas Kilroy, and Lieutenant Healy, expecting trouble, kept all their 160 men on hand.

Carrying banners and chanting "CIO, CIO," the strikers drew within a block and a half of the gate to find the police lined up awaiting them. Captain Kilroy stepped forward and asked the crowd to disperse.

"You can't get through here," he declared. "We must do our duty."

Jeers greeted his words. Then the demonstrators began hurling bricks, stones, and bolts.

The police replied with tear gas. The crowd fell back for a moment, choking, and then, the police say, began firing at the officers. The officers fired warning shots and, when, according to police, the strikers continued firing, they returned it.

Men began dropping on both sides. The strikers fell back before the police bullets and swinging police clubs.

Police wagons then raced onto the field and began picking up the injured. Some were taken to the Republic plant's emergency hospital, some to the South Chicago Hospital, and some to the Bridewell Hospital.

Most of the policemen who were injured were struck by steel bolts hurled by the strikers or shot from their slings.

from the New York Times, *May 31, 1937. Reprinted in Richard B. Morris and James Woodress, eds.,* Voices from America's Past, *vol. 3, The Twentieth Century (New York: Dutton, 1962), 111–112.*

Discussion Questions

1. What was the Memorial Day Massacre?
2. According to this account, who was responsible for the bloody clash—the strikers or the police?
3. This *New York Times* account supports the official police version, but eyewitnesses and photographs proved that the police brutally attacked the strikers. Who benefited most from the newspaper version, and why?

Name _____ Date _____

PRIMARY SOURCE WPA Posters

The Works Progress Administration (WPA) created jobs for more than 8 million people and found work for unemployed writers, artists, actors, and musicians. Many artists, for example, were paid to create posters like these advertising the WPA. What positive values of American culture do these posters convey?

The Granger Collection, New York.

Research Options

1. Investigate whether any murals or buildings—post offices, schools, airports, libraries, hospitals, and so forth—in your community were created through the WPA. Then work with classmates to create a map showing the sites of these projects.

2. The WPA employed artists and writers such as Ben Shahn, Jackson Pollock, Saul Bellow, and Richard Wright. Choose one artist, writer, actor, or musician who worked for the WPA and write a brief description of the works he or she created in the 1930s.

CHAPTER
15

Section 4

PRIMARY SOURCE *from Let Us Now Praise Famous Men*

In 1936 journalist James Agee and photographer Walker Evans researched rural life in America. Their collaboration, which was published in book form in 1941, yielded a record of the lives of three Alabama tenant families: the Gudgers, the Ricketts, and the Woods. According to this excerpt, what hardships did poor tenant farmers face?

What is earned at the end of a given year is never to be depended on and, even late in a season, is never predictable. It can be enough to tide through the dead months of the winter, sometimes even better: it can be enough, spread very thin, to take through two months, and a sickness, or six weeks, or a month: it can be little enough to be completely meaningless: it can be nothing: it can be enough less than nothing to insure a tenant only of an equally hopeless lack of money at the end of his next year's work: and whatever one year may bring in the way of good luck, there is never any reason to hope that that luck will be repeated in the next year or the year after that.

The best that Woods has ever cleared was $1300 during a war year. During the teens and twenties he fairly often cleared as much as $300; he fairly often cleared $50 and less; two or three times he ended the year in debt. During the depression years he has more often cleared $50 and less; last year he cleared $150, but serious illness during the winter ate it up rapidly.

The best that Gudger has ever cleared is $125. That was in the plow-under year. He felt exceedingly hopeful and bought a mule: but when his landlord warned him of how he was coming out the next year, he sold it. Most years he has not made more than $25 to $30; and about one year in three he has ended in debt. Year before last he wound up $80 in debt; last year, $12; of Boles, his new landlord, the first thing he had to do was borrow $15 to get through the winter until rations advances should begin.

Years ago the Ricketts were, relatively speaking, almost prosperous. Besides their cotton farming they had ten cows and sold the milk, and they lived near a good stream and had all the fish they wanted. Ricketts went $400 into debt on a fine young pair of mules. One of the mules died before it had made its first crop; the other died the year after; against his fear, amounting to full horror, of sinking to the half-crop level where nothing is owned, Ricketts went into debt for other, inferior mules; his cows went one by one into debts and desperate exchanges and by

sickness; he got congestive chills; his wife got pellagra; a number of his children died; he got appendicitis and lay for days on end under the ice cap; his wife's pellagra got into her brain; for ten consecutive years now, though they have lived on so little rations money, and have turned nearly all their cottonseed money toward their debts, they have not cleared or had any hope of clearing a cent at the end of the year.

It is not often, then, at the end of the season, that a tenant clears enough money to tide him through the winter, or even an appreciable part of it. More generally he can count on it that, during most of the four months between settlement time in the fall and the beginning of work and resumption of rations advances in the early spring, he will have no money and can expect none, nor any help, from his landlord: and of having no money during the six midsummer weeks of laying by, he can be still more sure. Four to six months of each year, in other words, he is much more likely than not to have nothing whatever, and during these months he must take care for himself: he is no responsibility of the landlord's. All he can hope to do is find work. This is hard, because there are a good many chronically unemployed in the towns, and they are more convenient to most openings for work and can at all times be counted on if they are needed; also there is no increase, during these two dead farming seasons, of other kinds of work to do. And so, with no more jobs open than at any other time of year, and with plenty of men convenient to take them, the whole tenant population, hundreds and thousands in any locality, are desperately in need of work.

from James Agee and Walker Evans, *Let Us Now Praise Famous Men* (Boston: Houghton Mifflin, 1941), 118–120.

Discussion Questions

1. What hardships did these three families face?
2. Which one of these families fared the worst? Explain.
3. What portrait of tenant farming does this excerpt portray?

CHAPTER

15

Section 3

LITERATURE SELECTION *from Hard Times*
by César Chávez

Hard Times is a collection of oral histories about life in the Depression-era United States. This account, told to collector Studs Terkel by César Chávez, gives details about the particular treatment of Mexican Americans which made hard times even harder. As you read, think about how Chávez's childhood experiences might have formed and shaped his adult life.

Oh, I remember having to move out of our house. My father had brought in a team of horses and wagon. We had always lived in that house, and we couldn't understand why we were moving out. When we got to the other house, it was a worse house, a poor house. That must have been around 1934. I was about six years old.

It's known as the North Gila Valley, about fifty miles north of Yuma. My dad was being turned out of his small plot of land. He had inherited this from his father, who had homesteaded it. I saw my two, three other uncles also moving out. And for the same reason. The bank had foreclosed on the loan.

If the local bank approved, the Government would guarantee the loan and small farmers like my father would continue in business. It so happened the president of the bank was the guy who most wanted our land. We were surrounded by him: he owned all the land around us. Of course he wouldn't pass the loan.

One morning a giant tractor came in, like we had never seen before. My daddy used to do all his work with horses. So this huge tractor came in and began to knock down this corral, this small corral where my father kept his horses. We didn't understand why. In the matter or a week, the whole face of the land was changed. Ditches were dug, and it was different. I didn't like it as much.

We all of us climbed into an old Chevy that my dad had. And then we were in California, and migratory workers. There were five kids—a small family by those standards. It must have been around '36. I was about eight. Well, it was a strange life. We had been poor, but we knew every night there was a bed *there*, and that *this* was our room. There was a kitchen. It was sort of a settled life, and we had chickens and hogs, eggs and all those things. But that all of sudden changed. When

you're small, you can't figure these things out. You know something's not right and you don't like it, but you don't question it and you don't let that get you down. You sort of just continue to move.

But this had quite an impact on my father. He had been used to owning the land and all of the sudden there was no more land. What I heard . . . what I made out of conversations between my mother and my father—things like, we'll work this season and then we'll get enough money and we'll go and buy a piece of land in Arizona. Things like that. Became like a habit. He never gave up hope that some day he would come back and get a little piece of land.

I can understand very, very well this feeling. These conversations were sort of melancholy. I guess my brothers and my sisters could also see this very sad look on my father's face.

That piece of land he wanted . . . ?

No, never. It never happened. He stopped talking about that some years ago. The drive for land, it's a very powerful drive. When we moved to California, we would work after school. Sometimes we wouldn't go. "Following the crops," we missed much school. Trying to get enough money to stay alive the following winter, the whole family picking apricots, walnuts, prunes. We were pretty new, we had never been migratory workers. We were taken advantage of quite a bit by the labor contractor* and the crew pusher. In some pretty silly ways. (Laughs.)

Sometimes we can't help but laugh about it. We trusted everybody that came around. You're traveling in California with all your belongings in your car: it's obvious. Those days we didn't have a trailer. This is bait for the labor contractor. Anywhere we

> *You know something's not right and you don't like it, but you don't question it and you don't let that get you down. You sort of just continue to move.*

* "That's a man who specializes in contracting human beings to do cheap labor."

stopped, there was a labor contractor offering all kinds of jobs and good wages, and we were always deceived by them and we always went. Trust them.

Coming into San Jose, not finding—being lied to, that there was work. We had no money at all, and had to live on the outskirts of town under a bridge and dry creek. That wasn't really unbearable. What was unbearable was so many families living just a quarter of a mile. And you know how kids are. They'd bring in those things that really hurt us quite a bit. Most of those kids were middle-class families.

We got hooked on a real scheme once. We were going by Fresno on our way to Delano. We stopped at some service station and this labor contractor saw the car. He offered a lot of money. We went. We worked the first week: the grapes were pretty bad and we couldn't make much. We all stayed off from school in order to make some money. Saturday we were to be paid and we didn't get paid. He came and said the winery hadn't paid him. We'd have money next week. He gave us $10. My dad took the $10 and went to the store and bought $10 worth of groceries. So we worked another week and in the middle of the second week, my father was asking him for his last week's pay, and he had the same excuse. This went on and we'd get $5 or $10 or $7 a week for about four weeks. For the whole family.

So one morning my father made the resolution no more work. If he doesn't pay us, we won't work. We got in a car and went over to see him. The house was empty. He had left. The winery said they had paid him and they showed us where they had paid him. This man had taken it.

Labor strikes were everywhere. We were one of the strikingest families, I guess. My dad didn't like the conditions, and he began to agitate. Some families would follow, and we'd go elsewhere. Sometimes we'd come back. We couldn't find a job elsewhere, so we'd come back. Sort of beg for a job. Employers would know and they would make it very humiliating . . . .

Did these strikes ever win?

Never.

> *If we were picking at a piece rate and we knew they were cheating on the weight, we wouldn't stand for it. So we'd lose the job, and we'd go elsewhere.*

We were among these families who always honored somebody else's grievance. Somebody would have a personal grievance with the employer. He'd say I'm not gonna work for this man. Even though we were working, we'd honor it. We felt we had to. So we'd walk out, too. Because we were prepared to honor those things, we caused many of the things ourselves. There were other families like that.

Sometimes when you had to come back, the contractor knew this . . . ?

They knew it, and they rubbed it in quite well. Sort of shameful to come back. We were trapped. We'd have to do it for a few days to get enough money to get enough gas.

One of the experiences I had. We went through Indio, California. Along the highway there were signs in most of the small restaurants that said "White Trade Only." My dad read English, but he didn't really know the meaning. He went in to get some coffee—a pot that he had, to get some coffee for my mother. He asked us not to come in, but we followed him anyway. And this young waitress said, "We don't serve Mexicans here. Get out of here." I was there, and I saw it and heard it. She paid no more attention. I'm sure for the rest of her life she never thought of it again. But every time we thought of it, it hurt us. So we got back in the car and what a difficult time trying—in fact, we never got the coffee. These are sort of unimportant, but they're . . . you remember 'em very well.

One time there was a little diner across the tracks in Brawley. We used to shine shoes after school. Saturday was a good day. We used to shine shoes for three cents, two cents. Hamburgers were then, as I remember, seven cents. There was this little diner all the way across town. The moment we stepped across the tracks, the police stopped us. They would let us go there, to what we called "the American town," the Anglo town, with a shoe shine box. We went to this little place and we walked in.

There was this young waitress again. With either her boyfriend or someone close, because they were involved in conversation. And there was this familiar sign again, but we paid no attention to it. She looked up at us and she sort of—it wasn't what she said, it was just a gesture. A sort of gesture of total rejection. Her hand, you know, and the way she turned her face away from us. She said: "Wattaya want?" So we told her we'd like to buy two hamburgers. She sort of laughed, a sarcastic sort of laugh. And she said, "Oh, we don't sell to Mexicans. Why don't you go across to Mexican town, you can buy 'em over there." And then she turned around and continued her conversation.

She never knew how much she was hurting us. But it stayed with us.

We'd go to school two days sometimes, a week, two weeks, three weeks at most. This is when we were migrating. We'd come back to our winter base, and if we were lucky, we'd get in a good solid all of January, February, March, April, May. So we had five months out of a possible nine months. We started counting how many schools we'd been to and we counted thirty-seven. Elementary schools. From first to eighth grade. Thirty-seven. We never got a transfer. Friday we didn't tell the teacher or anything. We'd just go home. And they accepted this.

I remember one teacher—I wondered why she was asking so many questions. (In those days anybody asked questions, you became suspicious. Either a cop or a social worker.) She was a young teacher, and she just wanted to know why we were behind. One day she drove into the camp. That was quite an event, because we never had a teacher come over. Never. So it was, you know, a very meaningful day for us.

This I remember. Some people put this out of their minds and forget it. I don't. I don't want to forget it. I don't want it to take the best of me, but I want to be there because this is what happened. This is the truth, you know. History.

Activity Options

1. With a classmate, role-play an interview between an oral historian and a person discussed by Chávez, such as one of his family members, a fellow worker, or someone who displayed the sort of prejudice that Chávez fought.
2. Draw a scene from Chávez's childhood. Create a caption for the scene that describes what Chávez learned or experienced.
3. Interview an older member of your family or community about their childhood. Focus the interview on issues of social justice, overcoming obstacles, and "life lessons" learned during the subject's youth.
4. Create a 1930s poster encouraging farm workers to protest mistreatment. What sort of protest will you encourage? Use persuasive language and include examples of the wrongdoings you attempt to challenge. You may wish to research the style of 1930s protest posters to make yours more realistic.

CHAPTER 15

Section 1

AMERICAN LIVES   Huey Long
Louisiana's "Kingfish"

"Why weep or slumber, America?/Land of brave and true/With castles, clothing and food for all/All belongs to you./Ev'ry man a king, ev'ry man a king."
—Huey Long, recitation at the end of a radio broadcast (1935)

Huey Long (1893–1935) was a skilled politician who used a populist message and political manipulation to win great power in Louisiana. As his popularity grew, he threatened Franklin Roosevelt's hold on the presidency—only to be cut down by a bullet.

Long was a debater in high school. He hoped to go to law school, but had to work. Juggling a job and high school, he earned his diploma. Then he completed a three-year course of law in just eight months. He was admitted to the Louisiana bar at 21. He quickly entered politics, winning election to the state railroad commission.

By 1928 Long was campaigning for governor. Louisiana suffered from underdevelopment. It had only 30 miles of paved roads, no bridges crossed major rivers, and many poor children could not attend school. Long promised to change that: "Give me the chance to dry the tears of those who still weep," he said. He won, and quickly made changes. In a few years, the state had 8,500 miles of roads and twelve new bridges. Children were put on school buses to get to school and given free textbooks once they got there. The free books went to parochial schools too. When that law was challenged in the U.S. Supreme Court, Long himself argued in favor of it and won.

Long achieved these goals while fighting a reluctant state legislature. Some objected to his goals, others to his tactics—which included using money and arm-twisting to convince legislators to vote his way. The legislature moved to impeach him, but key state senators refused to convict and Long was saved. He then won statewide election to the U.S. Senate, quieting his critics.

Long delayed moving to Washington to consolidate his power in the state. Opponents were harassed by government officials or by Long's police. He put judges favorable to him into the state courts. He controlled the state Civil Service Commission and used new laws to give himself power over every official—city, parish, or state—in Louisiana.

In Washington, many saw Long as a comic figure. Loud and brash, he was colorful. He called himself the "Kingfish" after a character on a popular radio show, and stories circulated about his disregard for social manners. About some things, though, Long was serious. For years he had campaigned in Louisiana to "make every man a king." He was ready to bring that message to the nation. At first he supported Franklin Roosevelt, but soon he came to believe that the New Deal did not go far enough.

He began a campaign to win the presidency. Long set up "Share Our Wealth" clubs across the country. He spoke far and wide of his plans to limit a person's income to no more than $1.8 million and to guarantee every adult no less than $2,000. He promised free education through college and pensions for the aged. He even wrote a book describing what he would do when president—*My First Days in the White House* (1935). Roosevelt and his aides worried that Long would run as a third-party candidate in 1936 and pull as many as six million votes—throwing the election into the House of Representatives.

In the fall of 1935, Long returned to Louisiana for a special session of the legislature. As he left the state capitol one evening, a man stepped from behind a pillar and shot him. The assassin—immediately shot dead by Long's bodyguards—was a doctor whose father-in-law, a judge, had been forced off the bench by Long. Two days later death claimed the "Kingfish," a man described by writer William Manchester in 1974 as "one of the very few men of whom it can be said that, had he lived, American history would have been dramatically different."

Questions

1. Evaluate Long as a reformer.
2. How did Long's plan to limit incomes violate the free enterprise system?
3. Why did Roosevelt worry about Long?

AMERICAN LIVES # Mary McLeod Bethune
Teacher to Blacks and Whites

"The true worth of a race must be measured by the character of its woman-hood."—Mary McLeod Bethune, speech titled "A Century of Progress of Negro Women" (1933)

Mary McLeod Bethune was dedicated to help-ing African Americans—especially African-American women. As an educator, organizer, and presidential advisor, she worked to end segregation and extend opportunities.

Bethune was born in 1875. She attended school and received training to be a teacher. Her goal was to begin missionary work in Africa, but her church turned down her request. For the next few years, she taught in various southern schools. In 1904, she settled in Daytona Beach, Florida, and started her own school. At the time, there were few public schools for African Americans in the South. Private schools like Bethune's were vital to educating blacks.

Bethune started her school with, she later said, "five little girls, a dollar and a half, and faith in God." She taught academic subjects, religion, and practical skills such as cooking and sewing. Although her son was one of her first students, Bethune planned from the start to serve girls pri-marily. She believed that opportunities for black females were severely limited and that women played an important role in society.

Bethune had to devote much time to raising money for her school. She baked and sold pies. She won contributions from black and white members of the community. With her untiring work, the school grew. It began to offer high school as well as ele-mentary school courses. By 1911, it gave students training in teaching and nursing. By 1923, the Episcopal Church agreed to sponsor the school and merged it with the Cookman Institute, a male school. The name was changed to Bethune-Cookman College in 1929. At that time, the school dropped its earlier grades and became a junior col-lege. By 1948, it had become a full four-year college.

As the school grew more secure, Bethune branched into her second career as a national leader of African Americans. As president of the National Association of Colored Women, she strengthened the organization to include 10,000 members. Then she founded and led the National Council of Negro Women (NCNW). She used the organization to combat segregation and lynching, to celebrate African-American achievement, and to open opportunities. As the United States entered World War II, Congress debated creating a women's army corps. Bethune won the right for African Americans to enter the corps.

Through her work in the NCNW, Bethune met and became close friends with Eleanor Roosevelt, wife of the President, Franklin D. Roosevelt. Soon she launched into her third career as a government official and presidential adviser. The President appointed her to the National Youth Administration (NYA). Bethune worked to ensure that the pro-grams created by the NYA for young people extended to African Americans. She won control of a special scholarship fund, making her the only African American in the government able to dis-pense money. Over time, she granted more than $600,000 in scholarships to black students.

Bethune did not stop with her NYA work. She gathered all the African Americans in the govern-ment into the Federal Council on Negro Affairs, dubbed "the Black Cabinet." The group met every week at her house to discuss issues. She then used her influence and political skill to lobby government agencies or to persuade the White House to act.

She believed that she held a "sacred trust" to present "the dreams and the hopes and the prob-lems" of African Americans to the White House. At the same time, she also represented the administra-tion to the black community. After World War II, she returned to Florida and spent time traveling—speaking and inspiring others to take action. She died in Daytona Beach in 1955.

Questions

1. Why were schools like Bethune's important for African Americans in the South?
2. How does the quotation at the top of the page explain the education Bethune provided?
3. How was Bethune a teacher to both African Americans and whites?

Answer Key

Chapter 12, Section 1
GUIDED READING

A. Possible answers:

1. Launched raids against suspected Communists, socialists, and anarchists; arrested, jailed, and deported suspected radicals

2. Looked foolish when his raids failed to turn up evidence of a revolutionary conspiracy

3. Used it as an excuse to harass anyone unlike themselves, including African Americans, immigrants, Catholics, Jews, union members, and intellectuals

4. The Klan members' racial violence and criminal activities turned many Americans against them.

5. Threatened public safety; appeared to be an act of communism or anarchism

6. Called in the National Guard to restore order, leading to the end of the strike

7. People believed the steel companies' propaganda linking the strikers and their leaders to communism; violence had broken out, which alarmed a public that was still ignorant of the severe working conditions in the mills.

8. Made a written plea for peace between the strikers and steel companies

B. Answers will vary widely depending upon the specifics noted.

Chapter 12, Section 2
GUIDED READING

A. Possible answers:

Arranged an international conference; proposed a ten-year halt to building warships; proposed a disarmament agreement; urged passage of the Kellogg-Briand Treaty, renouncing war

B. Answers:

1. U
2. U
3. B or F
4. F or B

5. U
6. U
7. G
8. F
9. G
10. U
11. U
12. G
13. B or F
14. F or B
15. U
16. U

C. Possible answers:

1. Jubilant, happy, optimistic
2. Upset, angry, bitter
3. Nativist, racist, nationalist, isolationist, negative
4. Selfish, self-serving, disrespectful, dishonest
5. Upset, embarrassed
6. Respectful, accepting, understanding, approving

D. Answers will vary widely depending upon the specifics noted.

Chapter 12, Section 3
GUIDED READING

A. Possible answers:

1. Automobiles: Helped the economy to boom; spurred the building of paved roads, service stations, garages, and so on; changed architectural styles; gave people greater freedom to travel; reduced the isolation of farm life; led to urban sprawl; gave Americans a new status symbol

   Company or Product: Model T Ford

2. Airplane industry: Established a new means of transportation for people and goods; gave people greater freedom to travel

   Company or Product: Lockheed Company

3. Alternating current: Made it possible to distribute electric power over greater areas; led to the electrifica-

tion of homes and widespread use of electrical appliances; made housewives' work easier, freeing them for other activities; led to more uniform, conformist lifestyles; helped the economy to boom

   Company or Product: Electric refrigerator

4. Advertising: Created greater demand for consumer goods; increased sales and profits; turned luxury items into necessities; helped the economy to boom

   Company or Product: Listerine

5. Installment plan: Helped the economy to boom; helped to create a false sense of prosperity; allowed people to buy goods over an extended period of time without having to put up much money at the time of purchase

   Company or Product: Automobiles

B. Possible answers:

- A growing income gap between workers and managers

- Lack of true prosperity in the iron and railroad industries

- Losses suffered by farmers and mining companies

- The possibility that installment buying was getting out of hand and that it represented a superficial prosperity

C. Answers will vary widely depending upon the specifics noted.

Chapter 12
BUILDING VOCABULARY

A.

1. f
2. d
3. e
4. b
5. a
6. c

B.

1. T
2. F—Anarchists were those who opposed all forms of government.
3. F—As secretary of state, Charles Evans Hughes urged the major powers of the West to destroy much

of their arms.

4. T

5. T

C. Answers will vary depending on the specifics noted.

Chapter 12, Section 2
SKILLBUILDER PRACTICE

Sample summary:

Advances in medical science and physics during the 1920s opened a path toward the future. Medical advances included improvements in brain surgery, the discovery of a way to add vitamin D to milk, the development of an iron lung, and progress in treating many diseases. Physicists made strides in understanding X-rays and toward the study of atomic structure. In addition, the first long-range television transmission took place between New York and Washington.

Chapter 12, Section 1
RETEACHING ACTIVITIES

1. An attempt by the U.S. attorney general to hunt down suspected Communists, socialists, and anarchists

2. Keeping blacks in a suppressed state, destroying saloons, opposing unions, and driving Roman Catholics, Jews, and foreigners out of the country

3. It limited immigration from each European nation to 2 percent of the number of its nationals living in the United States in 1890; people from eastern and southern Europe

4. Workers wanted the right to negotiate for shorter hours and a living wage, as well as union recognition and collective bargaining rights.

5. A work force made up increasingly of immigrants, who were willing to work in poor conditions; language barriers among immigrants kept them from unionizing; more factory jobs taken by farmers, who were used to relying on themselves; most unions excluded African Americans

6. mine workers', longshoremen's, and railroad porters' unions

Chapter 12, Section 2
RETEACHING ACTIVITIES

A.

1. Kellogg-Briand Pact

2. Dawes Plan

3. business affairs; social reform

4. Charles R. Forbes

5. Andrew Mellon

B.

1. F—Russia was not invited to the U.S.-sponsored Washington Naval Conference in 1921 because of its Communist government.

2. T

3. T

4. F—For his role in the Teapot Dome Scandal, Secretary of the Interior Albert B. Fall became the first sitting cabinet member to be convicted of a felony.

5. F—President Harding died while in office in August 1923, the victim of a heart attack or stroke.

Chapter 12, Section 3
RETEACHING ACTIVITIES

1. b

2. b

3. d

4. a

5. c

6. a

Chapter 12, Section 3
GEOGRAPHY APPLICATION

Responses may vary on the inferential questions. Sample responses are given.

1. The 1920s were a decade of great prosperity, with the economy reaching a peak in 1929. The 1930s were a decade of economic depression in which the U.S. economy began to recover slowly only to decline again near the end of the decade.

2. 1929; about 4.5 million; 20 years

3. 1929–1932

4. Automobile production was lower in 1932 than in any other year of the two-decade period.

5. 1923–1924, 1926–1927

6. The slow economic upturn of the 1930s was stalled by another downturn; the recession was not as great as the one in 1929–1932 but was more severe than the ones in 1923–1924 and 1926–1927.

7. The automobile had become indispensable to Americans, so when cars bought during the prosperous 1920s were wearing out after five to ten years, Americans bought new cars even though times were bad.

Chapter 12, Section 1
PRIMARY SOURCE

Vanzetti's Speech to the Jury

Possible responses:

1. He said he did not commit robbery or murder in Braintree or Bridgewater.

2. Vanzetti accused the judge of being prejudiced against him because of Vanzetti's radical principles. Vanzetti also accused the judge of openly declaring to friends his hostility "on the train, at the University Club, of Boston, on the Golf Club of Worcester."

3. He accused Katzmann of deliberately stirring up prejudice and turning the jury against him.

4. The "crimes" of being a radical and being Italian

5. Some students might agree, citing the fact that Sacco and Vanzetti were victims of the Red Scare and the accused in Salem were victims of witchcraft hysteria. Other students might disagree because of differences in the magnitude of the tragedies; only two men were executed in the Sacco-Vanzetti case, whereas the Salem witch hunt executed 20.

Chapter 12, Section 1
PRIMARY SOURCE

Report on the Steel Strike

1. Informally assess students' letters on the basis of clarity and persuasiveness.

2. Have students illustrate what a modern workday is like by making a calendar similar to the one the steel worker provided. Then encourage students to draw conclusions based on their comparisons.

Chapter 12, Section 3
PRIMARY SOURCE

Advertisement

1. Before students begin, encourage them to look at the visual image as well as the text. Students will likely find that the ad uses an image of a car racing a cowboy on a horse in Wyoming and persuasive language like "sassy" and "wild" to sell the idea of speed, power, and adventure. They will also find that the ad does not include "hard" facts about the car.

2. Informally assess students' comparisons. As an alternative, you may want to have them create an advertisement for a car today, using Ned Jordan's ad as a model.

Chapter 12, Section 1
LITERATURE SELECTION

The Big Money

1. Informally assess the clarity and historical accuracy of students' obituaries.

2. Students may research such artists or writers as Upton Sinclair, Katherine Anne Porter, Ben Shahn, or Woody Guthrie.

Chapter 12, Section 1
LITERATURE SELECTION

"Justice Denied in Massachusetts"

1. Students may say that the speaker is despondent, deflated, defeated, fatalistic, pessimistic, depressed, and forlorn.

2. Students may cite images such as the abandoned garden, the unfruited tree, and the cold, blighted earth.

3. Students will likely point out that both Millay and Dos Passos react bitterly to the executions of Sacco and Vanzetti, expressing feelings of

helplessness, hopelessness, anger, and disillusionment.

Chapter 12, Section 2
AMERICAN LIVES

Ernesto Galarza

Possible responses:

1. Galarza is saying that the characteristics of Mexican Americans that Anglos criticize are really ways of behaving that Mexican Americans have adopted because of how they are treated.

2. The farm workers had difficulty organizing because the growers had great economic power, the growers could hire braceros as strikebreakers, and the unions were more interested in supporting industrial workers.

3. Galarza was always interested in education, and he and his wife started a school when he was studying for his doctorate. He probably also believed that education would help Mexican Americans get ahead in the United States.

Chapter 12, Section 3
AMERICAN LIVES

Henry Ford

Possible responses:

1. Ford was paying far more than any competitor, which to many business owners didn't make any sense.

2. Ford was important for having revolutionized the industry with his assembly-line operations and producing a necessary item that the general public could afford.

3. Ford was both a good and bad employer. His $5 day wage was generous at the time. However, the Sociology Department intruded in workers' lives, and his company suppressed union organizing.

Chapter 13, Section 1
GUIDED READING

Possible answers:

1. a. Supporters: Many progressive reformers and religious groups; the Anti-Saloon League; the

Women's Christian Temperance Union; people who lived in the rural South and West; native-born Protestants

b. Why: Believed too much drinking led to crime, wife and child abuse, accidents on the job, and other social problems; drinking was sinful; the government should outlaw liquor to protect the public's health and morals

2. a. Opponents: Many liberals, conservatives, and intellectuals; immigrant groups; people who opposed the government's meddling in their lives

b. Why: Were tired of making sacrifices and wanted to enjoy life; didn't consider drinking sinful or unhealthy; resented the government's meddling in their lives

3. Prohibition ended because
   - local police and the federal enforcement agency were underfunded, understaffed, and overwhelmed.
   - drinkers and bootleggers found ways to evade the law, through speakeasies, home stills, smuggling, etc.
   - underworld gangs caused a rise in crime and lawlessness.
   - prohibition came to be seen as worse than the problems it was supposed to fix.

4. a. Supporters: Secular thinkers; moderate Protestants; liberal thinkers; American Civil Liberties Union; people who didn't interpret the Bible literally; people who believed in Darwin's theory of evolution

b. Why: Supported scientific thinking; believed in Darwin's theory of evolution; did not believe the Bible should be interpreted literally; were concerned about the growing political power of fundamentalists

5. a. Supporters: Protestant fundamentalists

b. Why: believed in creationism, the literal interpretation of Genesis; were skeptical of scientific knowledge; did not want evolution taught to their children

6. Scopes was found guilty and fined $100; the verdict was later

overturned, but the law outlawing teaching evolution remained on the books.

Chapter 13, Section 2
GUIDED READING

A. Possible answers:

1. Fashions: Brighter colors; shorter and looser-fitting dresses; stockings skin-toned instead of black; pumps instead of high-laced shoes; hair boyishly short and dyed jet-black instead of long and natural

2. Behavior: Flouting of tradition; greater assertiveness; smoking and drinking in public; dancing with abandon; casual dating

3. Attitude: Rebellious; youthful; pleasure-loving; fun-loving; relaxed; casual; assertive; daring; independent; equal

4. Work: More jobs available, including "women's professions" as well as work once reserved for men; a huge demand for clerical workers, store clerks, and assembly-line workers

5. Home: A reduced birthrate; wider availability of ready-made clothes and prepared foods; household labor simplified by social innovations and inventions; schools and various institutions handled more family tasks, such as looking after children and elderly parents; more free time and more choices; a view of marriage as an equal partnership; marriage based on personal choice

6. Negatives: Pressure of juggling both work and family, especially among working-class women; adolescent rebelliousness; the conflict between traditional attitudes and modern ways of thinking; the double standard; limited admissions to medical schools; few managerial jobs; inequality in the workplace; lower wages than men earned

B. Answers will vary widely depending upon the specifics noted.

Chapter 13, Section 3
GUIDED READING

A. Possible answers:

1. Enrollments: Before the 1920s, approximately 1 million high school students; during the 1920s, 4 million students

2. Courses: Before the 1920s, high schools catered to college-bound students; during the 1920s, they catered to broad range of students, including those interested in vocational training and home economics.

3. Immigrants: Before the 1920s, many immigrant students who spoke some English; during the 1920s, many who spoke no English

4. Financing: Before the 1920s, costs doubled from 1913 to 1920; during the 1920s, costs doubled again, totaling $2.7 billion a year by 1926.

B. Possible answers:

1. Magazines: *Time, Reader's Digest*

2. Radio: KOKA; Melody Maker

3. Sports heroes: Babe Ruth, Jack Dempsey, Gene Tunney, Helen Wills, Gertrude Ederle; Andrew Foster

4. Movies: *The Jazz Singer, Steamboat Willie*

5. Theater, music, and art: Eugene O'Neill, George Gershwin, Edward Hopper, Georgia O'Keeffe; *The Hairy Ape*

6. Literature: Sinclair Lewis, F. Scott Fitzgerald, Dorothy Parker, Edith Wharton, Willa Cather, Edna St. Vincent Millay, Gertrude Stein, Ernest Hemingway, John Dos Passos, Ezra Pound, T.S. Eliot; *Babbitt, This Side of Paradise, The Great Gatsby, The Age of Innocence, Barren Ground, My Ántonia, The Waste Land, Three Soldiers, The Sun Also Rises, A Farewell to Arms*

C. Students should note that Lindbergh piloted the first nonstop solo flight across the Atlantic.

Chapter 13, Section 4
GUIDED READING

A. Possible answers:

1. Du Bois and Johnson: National Association for the Advancement of Colored People (NAACP); encouraged peaceful protests against racial violence; campaigned for anti lynching laws; sought equal rights for African Americans

2. Garvey: Universal Negro Improvement Association (UNIA); "Black is beautiful"; mass meetings and parades; message of pride; believed that African Americans should build an independent nation in Africa; opposed racial integration; promoted African-American-owned-businesses

B. Possible answers:

African-American Writers

1. McKay: Poet; wrote militant verses urging African Americans to resist prejudice and discrimination

2. Hughes: Poet; known for poems that described the difficult everyday lives of working-class African Americans

3. Hurston: Writer of novels, books of folklore, poems, and short stories; known for works that portrayed the lives of poor, unschooled Southern African Americans

African-American Performers

4. Robeson: Major dramatic actor and singer known for his commanding stage presence

5. Armstrong: Jazz trumpet player; known for his astounding sense of rhythm and ability to improvise; went on to become one of the most important and influential musicians in the history of jazz

6. Ellington: Jazz pianist and composer; won renown as one of America's greatest composers

7. Smith: Blues singer; perhaps the most outstanding female vocalist of her time; in 1927, became the highest-paid black artist in the world

Chapter 13
BUILDING VOCABULARY

A.

1. d   5. h

2. g   6. a

3. f   7. c

4. b   8. e

B.

1. Scopes Trial

2. George Gershwin

3. Georgia O'Keeffe

4. Louis Armstrong

5. Bessie Smith

C. Answers will vary depending on the specifics noted.

Chapter 13, Section 3
SKILLBUILDER PRACTICE

Possible responses:

Conclusion 1: Young people in the 1980s admired material wealth.

Support: Murphy and Spielberg were chosen for their remarkable box-office success.

Support: The pope and Mother Teresa were the only ones who haven't gained personal wealth from their work.

Conclusion 2: Young people in the 1980s valued entertainment.

Support: There are four actors and one director on the list.

Support: The two musical entertainers on the list are big stars.

Chapter 13, Section 1
RETEACHING ACTIVITIES

1. Pro: people judged each other more by their accomplishments than by their background and tolerated a greater variety of lifestyles; con: life could be impersonal and frightening; the pace of life was more fast-paced than leisurely.

2. They believed that too much drinking led to serious social problems, including crime, wife and child abuse, and accidents on the job.

3. Many people continued to drink illegally and there was not enough of a force to stop the great amount of smuggling and illegal production of alcohol.

4. Gangs that formed to sell alcohol illegally began killing each other as they competed for profits.

5. They believed that the Bible was inspired by God, and thus its stories in all their details were true.

6. John Scopes was found guilty of violating the Tennessee law against teaching evolution and fined $100.

Chapter 13, Section 2
RETEACHING ACTIVITIES

A.

1. teaching; nursing

2. managerial

3. birth-control

4. smoking; drinking

5. household labor

B.

1. F—Teenagers in the 1920s spent less time with their families than in decades before.

2. T

3. T

4. F—Traditionalists in churches and schools opposed women's more freewheeling social behavior.

5. F—The nation's birthrate, which had been declining for several decades, dropped at a slightly faster rate during the 1920s.

Chapter 13, Section 3
RETEACHING ACTIVITIES

A.

1. f

2. d

3. e

4. a

5. b

6. c

B.

1. prosperous times and higher educational standards for industry jobs

2. It created the new phenomenon of the shared national experience, in which Americans across the country listened to the same shows and events.

3. American society had become too conformist and materialistic; people led empty lives in the midst of prosperity; war was a terrible thing that should not be glorified.

Chapter 13, Section 4
RETEACHING ACTIVITIES

A.

1. Great Migration

2. Marcus Garvey

3. anti-lynching

B.

Literature: Claude McKay—Jamaican novelist and poet whose militant views urged African Americans to resist prejudice and discrimination; Langston Hughes, poet who captured the spirit and determination of working-class African Americans; Zora Neale Hurston, novelist who portrayed the lives of poor Southern blacks; Performance: Florence Mills, Josephine Baker, and Mabel Mercer shine in the popular musical comedy Shuffle Along; Paul Robeson—became a major dramatic stage actor; Music: Louis Armstrong—became one of the most influential musicians in the history of jazz; Duke Ellington—won renown as one of the greatest jazz composers of his time; Bessie Smith—outstanding blues singer who gained enormous popularity

Chapter 13, Section 3
GEOGRAPHY APPLICATION

Responses may vary on the inferential questions. Sample responses are given for those.

1. Your flight will be very noisy and cold, with constant vibration, and you will probably become dizzy. It may take you a long time to reach your destination, since you could be bumped at one of the refueling

stops so that the plane can take on more mail.

2. Chicago—a little less than a day (24 hours); Denver—nearly two days (48 hours); Los Angeles—three days (72 hours)

3. Two; four

4. San Francisco and New York

5. About 46 hours; about 18 hours

6. The upper Great Plains between Minneapolis and Great Falls, Montana; the south central area between St. Louis and New Orleans; and the southern Atlantic Coast from Washington, D.C., to Jacksonville

7. By flying north to Chicago, then flying west by way of Des Moines and Omaha; by flying west to Kansas City, then north to Omaha and west to Cheyenne

Chapter 13, Section 1
PRIMARY SOURCE

Political Cartoon

Possible responses:

1. The growth of organized crime and increased violence in the United States

2. Crooked politics, bootlegging, obsolete legal procedure, racketeering, public indifference, romanticization of criminals, short sentences, and quick pardons

3. Harmful

Chapter 13, Section 1
PRIMARY SOURCE

The Scopes Trial

1. Before students begin, encourage them to find out more about the trial setting in order to lend authenticity to their staging of Darrow's cross-examination. Then informally assess their re-creation.

2. Informally assess students' discussion. Examples might include the debates over assisted suicide, abortion, and the teaching of evolution in the classroom.

Chapter 13, Section 3
PRIMARY SOURCE

An Interview with Charles A. Lindbergh

1. Students may list specific questions related to the flight, including what route he took, what the weather was like, how he prepared for the trip, how many miles he flew, what obstacles he encountered, why he undertook the flight, and so forth. Encourage them to use on-line as well as print resources to find answers.

2. Informally assess students' charts. Through their research, students will likely find significant differences in airplane dimensions, navigational equipment, design, and construction.

Chapter 13, Section 4
PRIMARY SOURCE

"When the Negro Was in Vogue"

1. Students will likely say that it had a thriving culture and was a place where whites came to enjoy black clubs, parties, and dances. Some students may point out that discrimination also flourished in Harlem.

2. Students may say that it seemed new, different, and exotic.

3. Students may suggest that African Americans could not attend clubs in their own community; whites visited Harlem to be entertained, not to understand the black community; whites made more money writing about blacks than blacks did.

Chapter 13, Section 1
LITERATURE SELECTION

Inherit the Wind

After students have read this selection, you may want to have them view the film *Inherit the Wind* starring Spencer Tracy and Fredric March.

1. Informally assess students' performances. As an alternative, you may want to involve the class in a performance of the entire play.

2. Guide students to see that the trial transcript and the play's dialogue are similar; however, the play involves fictional characters and

events drawn from the real-life trial and includes stage directions that indicate how characters speak and act. Have groups prepare a Venn diagram or two-column chart based on their discussions.

Chapter 13, Section 3
AMERICAN LIVES

Georgia O'Keeffe

Possible responses:

1. She felt that the style was too imitative—that it didn't reflect her interests or approach.

2. O'Keeffe seemed to be more interested in the natural world, as it was natural objects—flowers, the sky, bones—that she primarily painted.

3. O'Keeffe's work includes realistic paintings that are almost photographic and abstract images that focus just on the form and color of her subject.

Chapter 13, Section 4
AMERICAN LIVES

Louis Armstrong

Possible responses:

1. From Henderson's band, Armstrong learned to sight-read music and to appreciate strong ensemble playing.

2. Armstrong brought virtuoso solos to a prominent place in jazz. He also introduced scat singing.

3. He was African American in a time when few black artists enjoyed widespread exposure; his music remained popular long after rock 'n' roll had eclipsed jazz and swing in the mainstream.

Chapter 14, Section 1
GUIDED READING

A. Possible answers:

1. Industry: Key industries barely made a profit; some industries lost business to foreign competition and new American technologies; some industries suffered from declining demand for their goods after World War I; the coal industry declined because of the development of new sources of energy; new housing

starts declined, affecting other businesses that depended on home construction.

2. Agriculture: After World War I, demand for farm products fell drastically, as did prices; many farmers could not pay off their debts and lost their farms, which caused some rural banks to fail; Congress passed federal price supports for farm products, but President Coolidge vetoed them.

3. Consumer spending: By making credit easily available, businesses encouraged Americans to pile up a large consumer debt; faced with rising prices, stagnant wages, and high levels of debt, consumers decreased their buying.

4. Distribution of wealth: Nearly half of American families earned less than the minimum amount needed for a decent standard of living, while the rich got richer; this unequal distribution meant most consumers had too little money to buy the goods produced by American factories.

5. Stock market: Many investors engaged in speculation and buying on margin, fueling the market upward and generating great wealth, but only on paper; when the market crashed, many investors lost their life savings.

B. Answers will vary widely depending upon the specifics noted.

Chapter 14, Section 2
GUIDED READING

A. Possible answers:

1. Employment: Many people found themselves out of jobs for years; women, African-American men, and Mexican-American men were discriminated against in the workplace and became targets of hostility.

2. Housing: Many unemployed people lost their homes; many homeless lived in the streets or in shantytowns; many farmers lost their farms.

3. Farming: Farmland already exhausted through overproduction was hit with drought and winds, turning the plains into the Dust Bowl; dramatic

decreases in farm prices and income; many farmers lost ownership of their farms and were forced to become tenant farmers or farm laborers.

4. Race relations: Intense competition for jobs sparked existing racial resentments into open hostility and violence; in 1933, 24 African Americans were lynched; thousands of Mexican Americans left the U.S. voluntarily or were deported.

5. Family life: The Depression strengthened family ties, but also increased family tensions; some men abandoned their families, discouraged by their inability to provide for them; women also faced greater pressures to provide for themselves and their families.

6. Physical health: Poor and homeless people scavenged or begged for food or turned to soup kitchens and bread lines; poor diet and lack of health care increased rates of serious health problems; malnutrition and starvation grew more common.

7. Emotional health: Many people became demoralized; suicides and admissions to mental hospitals increased dramatically; people were forced to accept compromises that would affect the rest of their lives; some people came to want financial security more than anything else in life.

B. Answers will vary widely depending upon the specifics noted.

Chapter 14, Section 3
GUIDED READING

A. Possible answers:

1. Believed that a chief function of government was to encourage voluntary cooperation among competing interest groups; believed that the federal government should guide relief measures but not directly participate in them

2. Caution; urged key leaders to work together to provide solutions and to act in ways that would not make the economic situation worse

3. a. Economic situation: Continued to worsen; unemployment continued to rise; more companies went out of business; soup kitchens, shan-

tytowns, and hoboes became common; the misery of ordinary people continued to grow

  b. Voter response: Republicans lost control of the House of Representatives and saw their majority in the Senate dwindle to one vote.

4. a. Economic action: Directed federal funds into public works projects, such as Boulder Dam, to jump-start the economy and create jobs; backed a series of federal programs, including the Federal Farm Board, the National Credit Corporation, the Glass-Steagall Banking Act, the Federal Home Loan Bank Act, and the Reconstruction Finance Corporation

  b. Economy's response: Continued to deteriorate

5. a. Bonus Army action: Opposed immediate payment of bonuses to World War I veterans; ordered an infantry operation to close their Capitol Hill shantytown, leading to the gassing of 1,000 people, a baby's death, and public outrage

  b. Political effect: Damaged his public image; assured the victory of Democratic candidate Franklin D. Roosevelt in the 1932 presidential election

B. Students should note that the Reconstruction Finance Corporation provided emergency financing to banks and other large businesses to fuel business expansion and thereby pump new life into the national economy; its efforts were ultimately too little, too late.

Chapter 14
BUILDING VOCABULARY

A.

1. price-supports

2. Great Depression

3. Dust Bowl

4. Herbert Hoover

5. Reconstruction Finance Corporation

B.

1. T

2. F—Hoping to reduce the flow of goods into the country, Congress in

1930 passed the Hawley-Smoot Tariff Act, which established the highest tariffs in the nation's history.

3. T

4. F—Many investors in the late 1920s began buying on margin, or paying a small percentage of a stock's price as a down payment and borrowing the rest.

5. F—The group of World War I veterans who marched on Washington, D.C. to demand immediate payment of their war bonuses was known as the Bonus Army.

C. Answers will vary depening on the specifics noted.

Chapter 14, Section 2
SKILLBUILDER PRACTICE

Possible response:

These graphs show a correlation between the rate of unemployment and the levels of spending and income for the years 1929 through 1933. The unemployment rate rose sharply after the stock-market crash in 1929, year to year until 1932 when it continued to rise but less dramatically. Without jobs, increasing numbers of people lost income and spending power. The average yearly income per person dropped steadily. The year following the crash, the average dropped by nearly $100,000 dollars. The drop grew more significant each succeeding year until it again dropped, but much less sharply in the year 1932–1933. Also as the depression wore on the gap between income and spending narrowed to the point where consumers were spending nearly every penny they earned. Saving or investing money would have been nearly impossible.

Chapter 14, Section 1
RETEACHING ACTIVITIES

decline in new homes—led to job losses in many related industries; more Americans living on credit—put more people in debt, which led to a decline in consumer spending; uneven distribution of wealth—many people did not have the money to purchase the flood of goods from factories; stock market

crash—many Americans lost most of their savings; widespread bank closings—millions of Americans lost their savings accounts; worldwide depression—makes it difficult to sell American farm products and manufactured goods abroad; Hawley-Smoot Tariff—substantially raised protective tariffs, and increased unemployment in industries that could no longer export goods to Europe

Chapter 14, Section 2
RETEACHING ACTIVITIES

1. Many were farmers, who could at the very least grow enough food to feed their family; many city-dwellers had to beg and search for food.

2. Their unemployment rates were higher, they were often the lowest paid, and they had to deal with increasing prejudice and racial violence.

3. The plowing up of the protective layer of prairie grasses in order to create new farmland, left little grass and few trees to hold the soil down.

4. Many suffered from malnutrition and diet-related diseases; many were forced to leave school and work, while others ran away from home and wandered the country.

5. Many people believed that women, especially married women, had no right to work while so many men were out of work.

6. It led to a rise in suicides and admissions to mental hospitals; it caused many people to put off visiting the doctor or dentist, people also delayed college or marriage.

Chapter 14, Section 3
RETEACHING ACTIVITIES

1. c

2. a

3. a

4. b

5. d

6. a

Chapter 14, Section 2

GEOGRAPHY APPLICATION

Responses may vary on the inferential questions. Sample responses are given for those.

1. North Dakota, South Dakota, New Mexico, and Oklahoma

2. the part east of the Mississippi; The East had six states with unemployment rates of 10 percent or less and had only two states—West Virginia and Florida—with unemployment rates greater than 20 percent.

3. North Dakota, South Dakota, Nebraska, Kansas, and Oklahoma

4. Portland, Oregon (or the Pacific Northwest); Wyoming, Utah, Idaho, and Oregon

5. Los Angeles, California and the Pacific region; People from the Dust Bowl overwhelmed southern California, so many moved up the coast toward Washington, looking for shelter and work.

Chapter 14, Section 1
PRIMARY SOURCE

The Stock Market Crash

1. Figures will vary. Before students begin this activity, provide them with the business section of a national newspaper and guide them to understand how stock information is organized.

2. Through their research, students will find that on Black Monday the Dow plunged 508 points, the largest single-day drop in stock market history, and one-fifth of the paper value of stocks evaporated. Similarities: both crashes occurred in October and both involved a dramatic drop of stock prices. Differences: the 1929 crash helped precipitate the Great Depression, whereas the 1987 crash had no such long-term effects because of prompt government action to ease credit.

Chapter 14, Section 1
PRIMARY SOURCE

Political Cartoon

1. Diary entries will vary but should

include details about the stock market crash, the failure of banks, or another aspect of financial collapse as well as how this man felt about his own personal financial ruin.

2. Informally assess students' cartoons. You may want to have the class choose the three most effective cartoons or work together collaboratively to create a Great Depression comic book.

Chapter 14, Section 2
PRIMARY SOURCE

Letter from a Dust Bowl Survivor

Possible responses:

1. Keeping dust out of homes, schools, churches, and food; getting lost in dust storms; dealing with health problems such as pneumonia; being unable to plant crops

2. Some students may say that Grace was resigned to her plight during these "troublesome times." They may point out that she had adjusted to a new way of life, remaining indoors and only going outdoors when the dust storms let up. Others may infer that she was overwhelmed by the enormity of the problems caused by the dust storms. They may cite the fact that she anticipated suffering if relief didn't come soon.

3. Students may point out that a sense of humor, resourcefulness in coping with the dust, and hard work helped them survive the ordeal.

Chapter 14, Section 3
PRIMARY SOURCE

Attack on the Bonus Army

Possible responses:

1. A veteran was shot and killed by a Washington policeman during a skirmish to drive Bonus Army members out of a vacant house.

2. They advanced on the veterans with drawn sabers and fixed bayonets and then used tear gas to rout them.

3. Some students may say that the veterans were not treated fairly because they were in Washington to lobby for early payment of what was

rightfully theirs, not to start trouble. They may point out that the veterans fought for their country in World War I; it was wrong for their country to turn on them. Others may feel that the veterans were treated fairly because they refused to leave the capital after the issue of early payment had been decided. They may feel that the army, acting on the president's orders and acting in the interest of the public's welfare, had no choice but to use force to compel the veterans to leave.

Chapter 14, Section 2
LITERATURE SELECTION

In the Beginning

1. Before students begin, encourage them to draw on information in their textbooks in order to formulate an explanation that a child could understand. Then informally assess students' role-playing.

Chapter 14, Section 1
AMERICAN LIVES

Gordon Parks

Possible responses:

1. Parks's photos of the Brazilian boy helped save the boy's life.

2. When young, Parks experienced life among both the poor and the wealthy, which gave him understanding of both levels of society when taking pictures.

3. Parks seems to have been most successful as a photographer—where he has had a long career and won a fellowship—and as a movie maker—where he has won critical praise and audience acceptance.

Chapter 14, Section 1
AMERICAN LIVES

Alfred E. Smith

Possible responses:

1. As a state assembly member, he kept himself apart from identification with Tammany Hall corruption. As governor, he appointed Republicans and independents, not just Democrats.

2. Some people feared that he would take orders from the Pope.

3. Smith was also plagued by his identification with repeal of prohibition and by the economic success of the 1920s.

Chapter 15, Section 1
GUIDED READING

A. Possible answers:

1. Immediate: (Provided)

   Long-Term: (Provided)

2. Immediate: Established the FDIC

   Long-Term: To restore public confidence in banks

3. Immediate: Required corporations to provide complete information on all stock offerings

   Long-Term: To restore public confidence in the stock market

4. Immediate: Set prices; established labor standards

   Long-Term: To ensure fair business practices and to promote industrial growth

5. Immediate: Paid farmers to lower production

   Long-Term: To raise crop prices (and, thus, farm income)

6. Immediate: Built and repaired dams and other projects in the Tennessee Valley

   Long-Term: To create prosperity in the impoverished Tennessee Valley region

7. Immediate: Put young men to work on road-building and conservation projects

   Long-Term: To reduce unemployment

8. Immediate: Provided direct relief for the needy

   Long-Term: To provide for the basic needs of the people hit hardest by the Depression

9. Immediate: Provided money to states to create jobs

   Long-Term: To reduce unemployment

10. Immediate: Provided 4 million immediate jobs

Long-Term: To reduce unemployment

11. Immediate: Provided government loans to homeowners who faced foreclosure

Long-Term: To help families keep their homes

B. Students should identify Huey Long as a spokesman for the poor; a governor of Louisiana and, later, its U.S. Senator; and an early supporter of the New Deal who turned against Roosevelt. His Share Our Wealth proposal was extremely popular nationwide. He was assassinated in 1935 at the height of his popularity.

Chapter 15, Section 2
GUIDED READING

A. Possible answers:

1. Problems: Soil depletion; inability to buy land; squalid housing; dust storms; debt; bank foreclosures; lack of electricity

   Laws/agencies: Soil Conservation and Domestic Allotment Act; Resettlement Administration; Farm Security Administration; Farm Mortgage Moratorium; Rural Electrification Administration; Public Utilities Holding Company Act

2. Problems: Unemployment; poverty; hopelessness; loss of dignity; lack of spending money

   Laws/agencies: Works Progress Administration; National Youth Administration

3. Problems: Unemployment; poverty; hopelessness; loss of dignity

   Laws/agencies: Works Progress Administration

4. Problems: Unemployment; poverty; hopelessness; loss of dignity

   Laws/agencies: Works Progress Administration; National Youth Administration; Wagner Act (National Labor Relations Act); National Labor Relations Board; Fair Labor Standards Act; Social Security Act

5. Problems: Poverty; hopelessness; loss of dignity

   Laws/agencies: Social Security Act

6. Problems: Poverty; hopelessness; loss of dignity

   Laws/agencies: Social Security Act

B. Students should note that Eleanor Roosevelt traveled the country to observe social conditions; helped to shape New Deal policies; prodded her husband to appoint women to government positions; was a great advocate for poor people, women, and minorities.

Chapter 15, Section 3
GUIDED READING

A. Possible answers:

1. Appointees: Frances Perkins

   Gains: Women appointed to important federal positions; slight increase in the number of women working outside the home

   Problems: Discrimination in the workplace; discriminatory wages; discriminatory hiring practices

2. Appointees: Mary McLeod Bethune; William H. Hastie; Robert C. Weaver

   Gains: Increased political voice through greater access to the president; organizations created for tenant farmers

   Problems: Segregation; racial violence; racism; discrimination in all areas of life; poll taxes

3. Unions: Congress of Industrial Organizations

   Gains: Better working conditions; increased bargaining power; dramatic increase in union membership

   Problems: Strike violence; big business opposition to labor unions

4. Other groups: Southern whites; various urban groups; immigrants; various religious and ethnic groups

   Reasons: New Deal labor laws and work-relief programs aided many of them; Roosevelt made direct and persuasive appeals to them; Roosevelt appointed many officials of urban-immigrant backgrounds.

B. Students should note that Collier was commissioner of Indian Affairs and a strong advocate of Native American rights; he helped create the Indian Reorganization Act of 1934, which restored some reservation lands to tribal ownership.

Chapter 15, Section 4
GUIDED READING

A. Possible answers:

1. *Gone with the Wind:* Film (or novel)

   Who: Clark Gable; Vivien Leigh (or Margaret Mitchell)

   Theme: Life among Southern plantation owners during the Civil War

2. *Mr. Smith Goes to Washington:* Film

   Who: Frank Capra

   Theme: Honest, kindhearted people winning out over greedy special interests

3. *The War of the Worlds:* Radio drama (or book)

   Who: Orson Welles (or H. G. Wells)

   Theme: Martian invasion of Earth

4. *Waiting for Lefty:* Play

   Who: Clifford Odets

   Theme: Labor struggles of the 1930s

5. *Native Son:* Novel

   Who: Richard Wright

   Theme: Difficulties faced by a young man trying to survive in a racist world

6. *The Grapes of Wrath:* Novel

   Who: John Steinbeck

   Theme: Difficulties of Oklahomans who leave the Dust Bowl for California

7. *Our Town:* Play

   Who: Thornton Wilder

   Theme: Warmth and beauty of small-town life in New England

8. *American Gothic:* Painting

   Who: Grant Wood

   Theme: Two stern-faced farmers; rural life during the Depression

Chapter 15, Section 5
GUIDED READING

A. Possible answers:

1. Laws/agencies: Wagner Act; Fair Labor Standards Act; National Labor Relations Board

Effects: Standards for wages and hours; ban on child labor; rights to organize and bargain collectively; government mediation of labor disputes

2. Laws/agencies: Agricultural Adjustment Acts; Soil Conservation Service

   Effects: Aid to farmers; farm price supports; taught contour plowing, terracing, crop rotation

3. Laws/agencies: Securities and Exchange Commission; Glass-Steagall Banking Act; Federal Deposit Insurance Corporation

   Effects: Monitoring of the stock market; federal enforcement of laws regarding the sale of stocks and bonds; insurance on bank accounts

4. Laws/agencies: Social Security Act

   Effects: Federal government's acceptance of some responsibility for the social welfare of its citizens; old-age insurance program; unemployment compensation system; programs to aid families with dependent children and the disabled

5. Laws/agencies: Civilian Conservation Corps; Soil Conservation Service; Taylor Grazing Act; Tennessee Valley Authority

   Effects: Programs protecting the nation's natural resources, including farmland; prevention of floods and dust storms; more national parks and wildlife refugees; pollution

B. Answers will vary widely depending upon the specifics noted.

Chapter 15
BUILDING VOCABULARY

A.

1. b
2. a
3. c
4. a
5. c

B.

1. g   5. c
2. f   6. b
3. h   7. e
4. a   8. d

C. Answers will vary depending on the specifics noted.

Chapter 15, Section 1
SKILLBUILDER PRACTICE

The issue: Whether government should control access to materials on the Internet

Proponents

Who they are: Congress, President Clinton, certain parent organizations

Their arguments: The government should help parents monitor what children see on the Internet. Americans helped pay for developing the Internet so should be able to use it without being bothered by indecent materials.

Opponents

Who they are: American Civil Liberties Union, American Library Association, federal court in Philadelphia

Their arguments: The law violates First Amendment rights of free speech. Parents, not government, should monitor what kids see. There are software filters parents can buy that screen Internet material. Inappropriate material is only a very small part of the Internet.

Chapter 15, Section 1
RETEACHING ACTIVITIES

A.

1. "Brain Trust"
2. fireside chats
3. National Recovery Administration
4. separation of powers
5. nationalization

B.

1. F—The three main goals of the New Deal were relief for the needy, economic recovery, and financial reform.
2. T
3. T
4. F—The Twenty-first Amendment, passed in 1933, repealed Prohibition.
5. F—New Deal critic Dr. Francis Townsend argued that the Roosevelt Administration wasn't doing enough to help the poor and elderly.

Chapter 15, Section 2
RETEACHING ACTIVITIES

1. It marked the first time that most African Americans voted Democratic rather than Republican and the first time that labor unions gave united support to a presidential candidate.

2. Congress passed the Soil Conservation and Domestic Allotment Act, which rewarded farmers for practicing soil conservation methods; Congress approved the second Agricultural Adjustment Act, which brought back many features of the first AAA; the Roosevelt administration created the Resettlement Administration, which loaned money to farmers to become landowners.

3. Airport and road construction; writing guides to cities; collecting historical slave narratives; painting murals; performing in theater troupes around the country

4. Decreased the number of working hours per week, increased the minimum wage, and banned hazardous work for those under 18

5. The elderly, the unemployed, and the poor

6. It protected the right of workers to join unions and engage in collective bargaining; it prohibited unfair labor practices and established the National Labor Relations Board to monitor unfair labor practices.

Chapter 15, Section 3
RETEACHING ACTIVITIES

1. b
2. d
3. b
4. a
5. a
6. c

Chapter 15, Section 4
RETEACHING ACTIVITIES

A.

1. b

2. e

3. f

4. a

5. c

6. d

B.

1. It paid artists a living wage to produce public art and sought to increase public appreciation of art.

2. They sought escape from the harsh realities of the Depression as well realistic portrayals of the difficult time.

3. Much of the art and literature of the time was sober and serious, while movie and radio productions tended to be more escapist and upbeat.

Chapter 15, Section 5
RETEACHING ACTIVITIES

A.

1. stock market

2. social security

3. deficit

4. Glass-Steagall Act

5. World War II

B.

Supporters—the New Deal relieved much poverty and suffering the country while striking a reasonable balance between unregulated capitalism and overregulated socialism; opponents—conservatives thought it made the government too large and powerful, and stifled free enterprise and individual initiative; liberals thought it did not go far enough in socializing the economy and eliminating social and economic inequality.

Chapter 15, Section 5
GEOGRAPHY APPLICATION

Responses may vary on the inferential questions. Sample responses are given for those.

1. The Northeast

2. Vermont and Maine; the South, the Southwest, and the Northwest

3. About 1.5 times as great

4. He lost some of the farming states of the Midwest and the Great Plains, and his popular-vote margin shrank by more than 6 million.

5. 1936

6. The Republicans' inability to bring the country out of the Great Depression

7. The Democratic popular vote was slightly less than that in 1936, even though the total vote had increased by about 6 million votes, so Democratic support was clearly slipping.

Chapter 15, Section 5
OUTLINE MAP

1. About 400 miles; about 300 miles

2. Tennessee, Kentucky, North Carolina, Virginia, Georgia, Alabama, Mississippi

3. First—Fort Loudoun Dam, last—Kentucky Dam, southernmost—Guntersville Dam

4. Nickajack Dam

5. Nine

6. Possible response: The water runs downhill to the southwest, passing through four dams and entering Alabama. After passing through Guntersville Dam, the water travels northwest, passing through two more dams and reentering Tennessee. Then, after passing through Pickwick Landing Dam, the water travels almost straight north into Kentucky Lake. It passes through the last dam, Kentucky Dam, and reaches Paducah, where it enters the Ohio River. Finally, it travels west to the Mississippi River, where it is carried southward to Memphis.

Chapter 15, Section 1
PRIMARY SOURCE

Father Coughlin's Anti-New Deal Speech

1. Informally assess whether students accurately reflect the opinions of Coughlin and callers who either support or oppose the New Deal.

2. Students may point out that Coughlin believed New Deal programs did not do enough to help the poor. Some students may discount his objections, citing the positive impact that the New Deal had on millions of Americans. Other students may support his arguments, citing persistent economic problems such as high unemployment and the wide gulf between rich and poor.

3. Informally assess how effectively students deliver this speech excerpt.

Chapter 15, Section 3
PRIMARY SOURCE

The Memorial Day Massacre

1. A violent clash between Chicago police and striking steel workers

2. According to this account, the strikers were responsible because they were armed, marched on the plant to try to close it, ignored police orders, and then attacked the police.

3. Some students may say the police benefited most because they would not be blamed for police brutality. Others may say that the Republic Steel Company benefited most because this account drew negative attention to unions.

Chapter 15, Section 4
PRIMARY SOURCE

WPA Posters

1. Maps will vary. If no buildings or murals in your community were created through the WPA, then have students research the scope of WPA projects in general.

2. Informally assess students' descriptions to be sure that they are detailed, coherent, and are based on thorough research.

Chapter 15, Section 4
PRIMARY SOURCE

Let Us Now Praise Famous Men

1. Debts, sickness, poverty, unemployment for part of the year

2. Some students will say the Gudgers because they cleared the least amount of money yearly and faced debt one year in every three. Others will say the Ricketts because they went into debt after enjoying relative prosperity, suffered from ill health, and experienced the deaths of several children.

3. Most students will say it is a negative portrait because it reveals the cycle of abject poverty and hopelessness endured by many tenant families.

Chapter 15, Section 3
LITERATURE SELECTION

Hard Times

1. Informally assess students' oral interviews. The questioner should ask questions that are informed by the selection. The subject should create a character whose responses include and extend the information available in the excerpt.

2. Informally assess students' drawings and captions. Captions should be informative, and dramatic and should include clear and correct use of grammar.

3. You may wish to review students' questions and their choice of subjects before they conduct the interview. Evaluate questions for focus on social justice and formative experiences. You may have students tape-record, videotape, or transcribe their interviews.

4. Informally assess students' posters for historical details, clarity, and use of persuasive devices.

Chapter 15, Section 1
AMERICAN LIVES

Huey Long

Possible responses:

1. Long brought badly needed upgrades and reforms to Louisiana, improving the lives of citizens. However, he achieved some of this through strong-arm tactics, and it later seemed that power was what motivated him more.

2. The free enterprise system is built on the idea that people can earn and keep the benefits of their work and businesses. By putting a limit on earnings, Long violated that principle.

3. Roosevelt worried about Long because in the midst of the Depression his message of redistributing wealth could be appealing—which could endanger Roosevelt's reelection.

Chapter 15, Section 3
AMERICAN LIVES

Mary McLeod Bethune

Possible responses:

1. There were very few public schools for African Americans in the South, so private institutions such as Bethune's provided virtually the only opportunities for education.

2. Given the importance Bethune placed on women, it is not surprising that she would place strong emphasis on educating women.

3. Bethune taught African Americans in her school and through her organizing work. She taught whites through her work as an adviser to President Roosevelt and in her speaking.

CURRICULUM